LASERS AND ELECTRO-OPTICS R

ADVANCES IN
OPTOELECTRONICS RESEARCH

LASERS AND ELECTRO-OPTICS RESEARCH AND TECHNOLOGY

Additional books in this series can be found on Nova's website under the Series tab.

Additional e-books in this series can be found on Nova's website under the e-book tab.

LASERS AND ELECTRO-OPTICS RESEARCH AND TECHNOLOGY

ADVANCES IN OPTOELECTRONICS RESEARCH

MARCUS R. OSWALD
EDITOR

New York

For permission to use material from this book please contact us:
Telephone 631-231-7269; Fax 631-231-8175
Web Site: http://www.novapublishers.com

Library of Congress Cataloging-in-Publication Data

ISBN: 978-1-63321-211-4

Published by Nova Science Publishers, Inc. † New York

CONTENTS

PREFACE

The first chapter of this compilation on optoelectronics research provides the full, exciting story of integrated silicon light-emitting devices (Si-LEDs). Silicon is currently the most important semiconductor material. The book continues by discussing surpamolecular polymer semiconductors toward organic mechatronics; elastico-mechanoluminescent materials; and nonlinear and fluctuation phenomenaunder conditions of strong selective reflection in inclined geometry.

Chapter 1 - This chapter provides the full, exciting story of integrated silicon light-emitting device (Si-LEDs). Silicon is currently the technologically most important semiconductor material. Applications in semiconductor photonics seemed unlikely due to its indirect electronic band-gap, but the discovery of visible light emission from a silicon p-n junction biased in avalanche breakdown, in the past few years, stimulated intense and still-increasing research activity of optical-electronic integrated-circuits (OEICs) because of the full compatibility of silicon p-n junction with the standard complementary-metal-oxide-semiconductor (CMOS) process technology through monolithic integration. In this paper, some possible mechanisms that relate to this type of optical radiation are reviewed in detail, and a theoretical model that is consistent with the analysis of the light emission phenomenon observed in the metal-oxide-semiconductor field-effect-transistor (MOSFET) operating in the saturation region is proposed. As the title indicates, it is a comprehensive review from the fundamental science of MOS-like structures to the material and processing technology (i.e., standard silicon CMOS IC technology) to the optimized device design to the application for on-chip optical interconnection. Two major groups of readers will find this chapter valuable. One group is comprised of engineers and other professionals directly working in the semiconductor industry, whose work requires a good understanding of electro-optical modulation techniques. This group includes system and subsystem designers, product development engineers, and engineers who are exploring new modulator architectures and need to know the various modulation technologies available and the strengths and weaknesses of each technology. Technical managers and project managers in the optical communications will also find this chapter informative and helpful for gaining a high-level understanding of the advantages, trade-offs, and other relevant issues related to different silicon electro-optical modulator technologies. The other major group consists of scientific researchers, including graduate students, involved in fiber optics and fiber-optic communication research, especially in the field of silicon material based optical transmitters and optical modulators. Senior undergraduate students who are interested in silicon photonics, and those students working on relevant class projects, will also find this chapter beneficial.

Chapter 2 - Controllable noncovalent forces drive organic/polymer semiconductors into supramolecular organic devices with distinguishing functional features. Supramolecular polymer semiconductors (SPSs) have not only extraordinary optoelectronic characters, but also potentially self-assembly, soft and mechanical features, self-healing and stimuli-responsive behaviors. In this chapter, the authors explored a series of supramolecular approaches to plastic electronics and demonstrated the supramolecular resistive switching and supramolecular electroluminescence. Firstly, π-stacked polymer semiconductors exhibit two supramolecular features: the reversible conformational change and the behaviors of molecular tweezers. Hindrance-functionalized stacked polymers were explored to apply for host materials in polymer light-emitting devices (PLEDs) and resistive switching materials in polymer nonvolatile flash memory. Secondly, the authors found the polyfluorene gels in 1,2-dichloroethane (DCE) at room temperatures with the feature emission peak at ~476 nm. Polyfluorenol-based supramolecular conjugated polymers (SCPs) exhibit the strong molecular assembled ability into gels, nanoparticles (nanogels) and aggregate bulk homojunction thin-films. Rather than ketone defect, aggregate mechanism of g-band at ~530 nm in PLEDs were supported by strong green emission of polyfluorenol-based SCPs in solution. PPFOH exhibit the color-tunable supramolecular (electro)luminescence in solutions, thin films and devices, ranging from blue, green, yellow, orange to white color by changing the molecular weight and formula solvents. The authors believe that SPSs and supramolecular mechatronics will become the cornerstone of organic learning mechano-devices to activate molecular consciousness toward organic intelligence robotics that will make one powerful science solution to social society in the 21st century.

Chapter 3 - Elastico-mechanoluminescence (EML) materials are a newly developed type of mechano-optical convertible inorganic phosphors. They can respond to different mechanical stress stimuli such as touch, impact, vibration, friction, stretching, compression, bend, and twist as light emission. More importantly, these materials possess an accurate linear dependence of EML intensity on the stress parameters (including intensity, energy and deformation rate) in the elastic limit. A stress sensitive coating prepared by the homogeneous dispersion of the EML indicators into an optical binder matrix can simultaneously "feel" (sense) and "see" (image) various mechanical stresses over a wide energy and frequency range. The EML intensity distribution directly reflects the stress distribution of the coating subjected to stresses. In view of the advantages of wireless, non-destructive, reproducible, real-time and reliable *in situ* stress sensing, EML materials have important application prospects as stress probe in the stress detecting field of life sciences, robot manufacturing, construction safety monitoring, aeronautics and astronautics. However, the research history on EML is relatively short, only about fifteen years since EML was first reported in 1999. There are still several urgent problems to be resolved before the wide practical applications of EML materials could be realized. In this chapter, the EML materials and EML development history are briefly introduced. Subsequently, the preparation method of EML materials and coating, the EML properties, mechanism, and applications are summarized. Finally, the challenges and perspectives of EML materials are discussed.

Chapter 4 - This chapter is devoted to investigation of the strong selective reflection of an obliquely incident laser beam (inclined geometry) from the interface "glass - rubidium vapour". Passages from the resonance Brewster reflection to the resonantly frustrated total internal reflection (TIR), caused by the frequency tuning of the incident radiation, are demonstrated experimentally. The intensity of the reflected light at these passages changes in more than 20 times. The contrast of the strongest reflection resonances exceeds 500% at the moderate heating of reflecting cells. A simple theory, which is based on a two-level model for resonance atoms and Fresnel formulas for reflection coefficients, is presented. Numerical calculations based on the proposed theory confirm main experimental results.

The controlling of the intensity and fluctuations of the selective reflected light was also investigated at the optical saturation of the resonance transitions.

The relative reduction of the intensity fluctuations is recorded in reflected light compared with the incident one. It is shown also that the optical saturation of selective reflection resonances leads to the appearance in the reflection spectra of new nonlinear structures. On conditions of frustrated TIR the asymmetry of saturation of hyperfine components D2-line in a natural abundance of rubidium isotopes is registered.

The noise of single-mode semiconductor laser with an external optical feedback is studied. The totally single-mode quantum lasing (TSQL) with a complete suppression of all system of subthreshold modes, including the subthreshold side modes of the laser's own cavity and the noisy modes of the external cavity is theoretically predicted and experimentally realized. The realized TSQL is characterized by a squeezed photon fluctuations in comparison with classical (coherent) light.

The selective reflection spectra are described where the frequency of lasing mode of the used semiconductor laser was jumplike retuned over the modes of the external (long) cavity. In this case, the characteristic steps— intensity quasilevels—arise on the reflectivity resonances. Low-noise reflectivity regimes with different sensitivities to external signals are found on these quasilevels.

In the final part of the chapter the possibility of reducing the quantum fluctuations for selectively reflected light on conditions of optical saturation of resonance transitions is explored. The single-mode semiconductor laser with external cavity has been used as a light source. When the laser is tuned according to the quasilevels, which have minimum intrinsic noise, the squeezing of amplitude quantum fluctuations of the selectively reflected radiation relative to the incident coherent light has been recorded.

The investigations in this chapter complement the optoelectronics, classical and quantum optics, and they can be useful for the further development of these disciplines.

In: Advances in Optoelectronics Research   ISBN: 978-1-63321-211-4
Editor: Marcus R. Oswald   © 2014 Nova Science Publishers, Inc.

Chapter 1

HOT CARRIER LUMINESCENCE IN SILICON METAL OXIDE SEMICONDUCTOR FIELD EFFECT TRANSISTOR

Kaikai Xu[1,2,3*]

[1]Department of Electrical Engineering and Computer Science, University of California, Irvine, California, US
[2]Integrated Nanosystems Research Facility (INRF), University of California, Irvine, California, US
[3]California Institute for Telecommunications and Information Technology (Calit2), Irvine, California, US

ABSTRACT

This chapter provides the full, exciting story of integrated silicon light-emitting device (Si-LEDs). Silicon is currently the technologically most important semiconductor material. Applications in semiconductor photonics seemed unlikely due to its indirect electronic band-gap, but the discovery of visible light emission from a silicon p-n junction biased in avalanche breakdown, in the past few years, stimulated intense and still-increasing research activity of optical-electronic integrated-circuits (OEICs) because of the full compatibility of silicon p-n junction with the standard complementary-metal-oxide-semiconductor (CMOS) process technology through monolithic integration. In this paper, some possible

* Corresponding author: Email: kaikaix@uci.edu.

mechanisms that relate to this type of optical radiation are reviewed in detail, and a theoretical model that is consistent with the analysis of the light emission phenomenon observed in the metal-oxide-semiconductor field-effect-transistor (MOSFET) operating in the saturation region is proposed. As the title indicates, it is a comprehensive review from the fundamental science of MOS-like structures to the material and processing technology (i.e., standard silicon CMOS IC technology) to the optimized device design to the application for on-chip optical interconnection. Two major groups of readers will find this chapter valuable. One group is comprised of engineers and other professionals directly working in the semiconductor industry, whose work requires a good understanding of electro-optical modulation techniques. This group includes system and subsystem designers, product development engineers, and engineers who are exploring new modulator architectures and need to know the various modulation technologies available and the strengths and weaknesses of each technology. Technical managers and project managers in the optical communications will also find this chapter informative and helpful for gaining a high-level understanding of the advantages, trade-offs, and other relevant issues related to different silicon electro-optical modulator technologies. The other major group consists of scientific researchers, including graduate students, involved in fiber optics and fiber-optic communication research, especially in the field of silicon material based optical transmitters and optical modulators. Senior undergraduate students who are interested in silicon photonics, and those students working on relevant class projects, will also find this chapter beneficial.

1. INTRODUCTION

Silicon is the material par excellence. It is the most widely studied material in the history of civilization. In fact, the present-day information age has dawned with an electronics revolution brought about by the maturity of silicon-based microelectronics [1].

Although silicon is currently the technologically most important semiconductor material, applications of it in semiconductor photonics seemed unlikely due to its indirect electronic bandgap. Various attempts have been made in the studies of Si light source, such as porous Si [2–4], erbium doping in Si[5], and Si-Ge island on Si-substrate [6]. For Si-Ge LED, to overcome the silicon band-gap discontinuity that occurs at the interface and enable intraband transitions of terahertz laser emission in simple quantum well configurations, Si-Ge system has been used [7]. To enhance the output efficiency of photoluminescence, more complicated Si-Ge LED with quantum cascade geometries is proposed [8], and tensile-strained technology has been chosen to construct an analog direct gap in SiGe material [9]. For Si LED with Er^+ doping, a silicon transistor with metal-insulator-structure (MIS) is proposed while Er^+ is implanted into the SiO_2 insulated layer to stimulate photons for advancing light emitting performance [10].

Among these studies, the most dazzling achievement in Si-based LED is the first continuous-wave Raman laser [11]. A Raman amplifier integrated with an external fiber-based optical feedback had been shown to yield optically pumped Raman lasing in Si [12]. Other progresses include III-V group material quantum wells' LED on bulk silicon platform [13] and silicon nano-particles in Si-in-SiN_x thin films [14]. Although these devices mentioned above have relatively high efficiency suitable for high performance optic fiber communication system as the excellent transmitters, they are not the best choice of light source for short-distance optical interconnection. One disadvantage of these devices is that the fabricating process is too complicated to be achieved by standard Si-CMOS technology only; another one is that the hybrid integration of non-silicon light source and silicon photo-receiver circuit is much more expensive than the monolithic integration of silicon light source and silicon receiver circuit.

On the contrary, the discovery of electroluminescence observed in silicon diode in avalanche breakdown was first reported in [15] although the silicon material is with an indirect bandgap structure. Further study in visible light from reverse-biased silicon p-n junctions was discussed by [16]. At an early stage, it was predicted that the mechanism of such optical emission should be attributed to the Bremsstrahlung radiation [17], which is an electromagnetic radiation produced by the deceleration of a charged particle when deflected by another charged particles, typically a carrier (generated in depletion region due to avalanche) by an atomic nucleus (immobile charge centers in depletion region). Consequently, the moving particle in the micro-plasma like depletion region will lose some kinetic energies, which is converted into the photons. Further investigation and discussion of the silicon diode light-emitting device are presented in [18–21] with the measured results that the optical emission power is closely dependent on the breakdown current with a relationship that is approximately linear. In other words, it implies that the number of carriers will determine the number of photons emitted out.

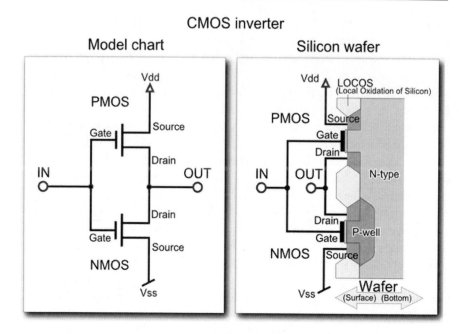

Figure 1. Typical layer and structure used in CMOS integrated circuits [22].

It is very important to note that silicon diode (i.e., a p-n junction diode) can be processed by the standard complementary-metal-oxide-semiconductor (CMOS) process technology very easily. It is noted that CMOS is a technology for constructing integrated circuits. The words "complementary-symmetry" refer to the fact that the typical digital design style with CMOS uses complementary and symmetrical pairs of p-type and n-type metal oxide semiconductor field effect transistor (MOSFETs) for logic functions which is shown in Figure 1.

In this paper, some possible mechanisms that relate to this type of optical radiation are reviewed in detail, and a theoretical model that is consistent with the analysis of the light emission phenomenon observed in the metal-oxide-semiconductor field-effect-transistor (MOSFET) operating in the saturation region is proposed. The chapter is structured as follows. Section 2 describes the possible origins of the visible light emission observed in the reverse-biased silicon p-n junctions and proposes a new analytical equation that enables the understanding of the correlation between hot carriers and emitted photons. Details of the light emission from the Si MOSFET device operating in the saturation region are described in Section 3 by means of channel current induced photon emission. Since the integration of silicon light sources with silicon microelectronics could lead to inexpensive optical displays and offer the potential for next-generation VLSI-compatible optical interconnect systems, Section 4 shows the need for an efficient Si-based on-chip light source for application in integrated optics as well as optical sensors. Finally, Section 5 makes a conclusion.

2. ANALYSIS OF THE MECHANISMS OF THE OPTICAL RADIATION

The phenomenon of light emission from avalanche silicon p-n junctions has been studied extensively since long time ago. Accordingly, the physical mechanisms of photon generation in the avalanching region have been discussed and modeled by numerous researchers. Despite the uncertainty and complication of the exact origin of this type of optical radiation, three theories have been proposed to explain this optical phenomenon: conduction-band to valence-band (*c-v*) radiation, conduction-band to conduction-band (*c-c*), and valence-band to valance-band (*v-v*). More specifically, the following processes can be concluded as the major reasons involved

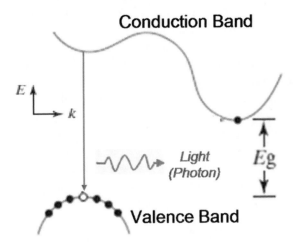

Figure 2. Direct-interband transition.

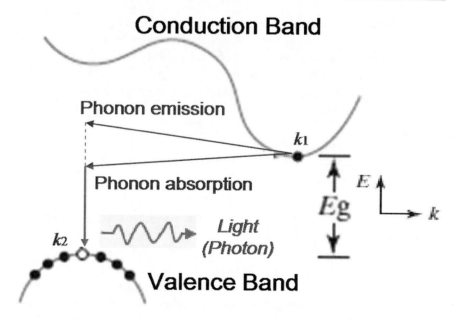

Figure 3. Indirect-interband transition.

- Intraband transitions (i.e., *c-c* or *v-v*) of electrons or holes within their respective band [23, 24]. For example, a hole radiatively transits between the light-hole band and the heavy-hole band [25].
- Direct or indirect interband recombination (i.e., *c-v*) of energetic electrons in the conduction band with holes in the valence band [26]. For example, a hot electron is radiatively recombined with a free hole [23]. Moreover, the phonon-assisted electron-hole recombination is the appropriate model for indirect band-gap materials such as silicon.
- Bremsstrahlung radiation due to the scattering of the hot electrons by charged Coulombic centers. It should be noted that the intraband transition consists of two types: direct and indirect. In fact, the indirect intraband transition is the so-called Bremsstrahlung mechanism [24].

In summary, these types of the process of recombination in the silicon band-structure model are presented in Figure 2–5.

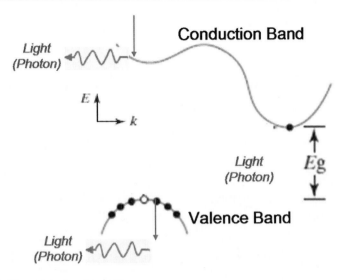

Figure 4. Direct-intraband transition.

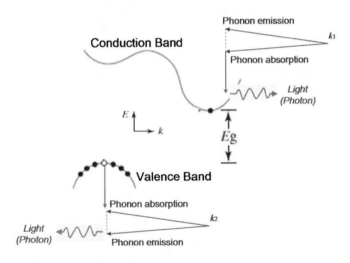

Figure 5. Indirect-intraband transition.

In order to calculate the light emission intensity for the various optical mechanisms mentioned above, the photon emission rate is given by

$$R = v\frac{C}{4\pi}\sum_{u,l}\int d\Omega_v \sum_{\lambda,k_u,k_l} M_\lambda\left(u,l,k_u,k_l,v\right) f_u\left(E_u\left(k_u\right)\right) \times f_l\left(E_l\left(k_l\right)\right)\delta\left(E_f - E_i\right) \tag{1}$$

where $f\left(E_i\left(k\right)\right)$ denotes the distribution function for electrons of band index i and wave vector k, parameters u and l indicate the upper and lower band indices for the transition of $\bar{f} = 1 - f$, respectively, v is the optical frequency, and C is a constant factor that is proportional to the product of the optical densities of state. Since Eq. (1) consists of both the direct transition rate and the indirect transition rate, the numerical expressions for the two rates above can be given by the following two equations [27]

$$R_{direct}\left(v\right) = 32vC\sum_{ul}\frac{V}{8\pi^3}\int_{RZ} d^3kf_u\left(E_u\left(k\right)\right)\bar{f}_l\left(E_l\left(k\right)\right)\sum_{i=1}^{3}\left|\left\langle u\left|\nabla_i\right|l\right\rangle\right|^2\delta\left(E_l\left(k\right) - E_u\left(k\right) + hv\right) \tag{2}$$

for spontaneous-emission rate for direct transition, and

$$R_{indirect}\left(v\right) = 32vC$$
$$\sum_{ul}\frac{V}{\left(8\pi^3\right)^2}\left(\int_{RZ} d^3k_l S_l\left(v,k_l\right)\int_{BV} d^3k_u + \int_{RZ} d^3k_u S_u\left(v,k_u\right)\int_{BZ} d^3k_u\right) \tag{3}$$
$$\times \bar{f}_l\left(E_l\left(k_l\right)\right)f_u\left(E_u\left(k_u\right)\right)\left|\left\langle k_u\left|H_p\right|k_l\right\rangle\right|^2\delta_{if}$$

for indirect-photon-emission rate. Note that the parameters $\bar{f}_l$, S_n, and δ_{if} are given respectively by

$$\bar{f}_l\left(E_l\left(k_l\right)\right) = 1 - f_l\left(E_l\left(k_l\right)\right) \tag{4}$$

$$S_n\left(v,k\right) = \sum_{i=1}^{3}\left|\sum_{m}\frac{\left\langle mk\left|\nabla_i\right|nk\right\rangle}{E_n\left(k\right) - E_m\left(k\right) - hv}\right|^2 \tag{5}$$

$$\delta_{if} = \delta\left(E_l\left(k_l\right) - E_u\left(k_u\right) + h\left(v + v_p\right)\right) + \delta\left(E_l\left(k_l\right) - E_u\left(k_u\right) + h\left(v - v_p\right)\right) \tag{6}$$

According to the probability of electron-hole recombination under indirect transition and substituting the density of state that is closely related to the constant C, the indirect-photon-emission rate in Eq. (2) becomes [28]

$$R(hv) = \frac{32\pi^3}{c^3 h^4} n^2 (hv)^2 \left[hv \frac{dn}{d(hv)} + n \right] \times$$

$$\int_{E_v} \int_{E_c} \exp\left[-\frac{(E_c - E_v - \Delta E)}{kT} \right] \times \sqrt{(-E_v)(E_c - E_g)} \times \delta(E_v - E_c + hv \pm k\theta) \, dE_c dE_v \quad (7)$$

where n is the refractive index of silicon, $\Delta E = E_{Fn} - E_{Fp}$ is the difference between the n-type semiconductor's quasi-Fermi level for electrons and the p-type semiconductor's quasi-Fermi level for holes, T is the lattice temperature, E_g is the energy band-gap, and $k\theta$ is the energy of phonon. The lower edge of the conduction band E_c designates the potential energy of an electron and the upper edge of the valence band E_v designates the potential energy of a hole. Solving Eq. (7) by integrating emission with absorption phenomena, the optical emission power per unit optical frequency in total can be expressed as [29]

$$I_{relative} = I_{emission} - I_{absorption} \quad (8)$$

where

$$I(v)_{emission} \sim n^2 (hv)^2 \left(hv + k\theta - E_g \right) \times$$

$$\exp\left[\frac{1}{k_0}(hv + k\theta)\left(\frac{1}{T_h} - 1 \right) + \frac{\Delta E}{T} - \frac{1}{2}(hv + k\theta - E_g)\left(\frac{1}{T_e} + \frac{1}{T_h} \right) \right] \times$$

$$\frac{aI_1}{2}(hv + k\theta - E_g) \quad (9)$$

and

$$I(v)_{absorption} \sim n^2 (hv)^2 (hv - k\theta - E_g) \times$$

$$\exp\left[\frac{1}{k_0}(hv - k\theta)\left(\frac{1}{T_h} - 1\right) + \frac{\Delta E}{T} - \frac{1}{2}(hv - k\theta - E_g)\left(\frac{1}{T_e} + \frac{1}{T_h}\right)\right] \times \qquad (10)$$

$$\frac{aI_1}{2}(hv - k\theta - E_g)$$

where $k\theta = -\frac{1}{2}\left((hv)_{emission} - (hv)_{absorption}\right)$ is the energy of the phonon, and I_1 is the modified Bessel function of the order of 1. Moreover, k is the Boltzmann's constant and θ is the angle between the electric field (i.e., Coulomb field) and the electron/hole velocity. For θ, it is known that both the nuclear (i.e., the Coulomb charged centers or artificial atoms in the depletion region of p-n junction) and electron spin degrees of freedom in silicon nanostructures is able to be manipulated by the hyperfine interaction in which the electron transport in quantum dots is localized [30]. Subsequently, if the Boltzmann approximation is applied, the hot-carrier distribution will be of the form below [31]

$$f(E) \sim \exp\left(-\frac{E}{W}\right)\left[1 - \frac{\overline{E_i}\left(\frac{E}{W}\right)}{\overline{E_i}\left(\frac{E_0}{W}\right)}\right] \qquad (11)$$

where $W \equiv kT_e$ is the electron energy, $\overline{E_i}$ is the transient energy of the carrier, and E_0, the energy of impact ionization at threshold, is about 1.5 times of the silicon band-gap energy E_g. Beyond the threshold energy, avalanche process with visible light emission from the reverse-biased p-n junctions will be observed. In result, Eq. (11) can be reduced to be

$$f(E) \sim \exp\left(-\frac{E}{kT_e}\right) \qquad (12)$$

which is a quasi-Maxwell's distribution that is similar to the energy distribution function of photon intensity if the photon-emission mechanism is simply assumed to be Bremsstrahlung radiation only [32]. On the other hand, the distribution of hot-carrier can be expressed in terms of the acoustic phonon which assists electron-hole recombination in the indirect interband transition process mentioned previously because the energy of hot-carrier can be expressed as [33]

$$E = \left(kT_e\right)\left(\frac{3\pi\mu_0 \mathrm{E}}{8s^2}\right) \tag{13}$$

where μ_0 is the mobility, E is the electric field, and s is the sound speed. Substituting Eq. (13) into Eq. (12), it follows that

$$f\left(E\right) \sim \exp\left(\frac{3\pi\mu_0 \mathrm{E}}{8s^2}\right) \tag{14}$$

According to the correlation between the effective temperature T_e and the mean-free-path λ_m and the correlation between the sound speed and the energy of phonon, the electron energy $W \equiv kT_e$ becomes [34]

$$W = \frac{\left(q\mathrm{E}\lambda_m\right)^2}{3\left(1-\cos\theta\right)E_{phonon}} \tag{15}$$

where E_{phonon} is the longitudinal acoustic phonon energy. Multiplying Eq. (7), Eq. (8), Eq. (11), and Eq. (15), the final predicted rate of photon-emission with the evidence of the absorption of photons by silicon itself being taken into account is obtained in the form below [35]

$$R_s = R_0\left(hv\right)\exp\left[-\alpha\left(hv\right)X_j\right] \tag{16}$$

where X_j is the junction depth, and R_0 is the rate of photon-emission at the beginning without any absorption. Assuming the assistance of phonon in the indirect recombination is taken into account, the absorption coefficient

$\alpha(hv)$, which is temperature dependent, for a given wavelength (or frequency v) is given by [36]

$$\alpha(hv) = C_1 \left[\frac{\left(hv - E_g + E_{phonon}\right)^2}{\exp\left(\frac{E_{phonon}}{kT_e}\right)} + \frac{\left(hv - E_g - E_{phonon}\right)^2}{1 - \exp\left(-\frac{E_{phonon}}{kT_e}\right)} \right] \quad (17)$$

where C_1 is a constant factor that is equal to the value of $\alpha(hv)$ at the effective temperature $T_e = 300K$ [37]. In addition, the temperature dependence on the band-gap energy E_g can be expressed as

$$E_g(T_e) = E_g(0) - \frac{aT_e^2}{b + T_e} \quad (18)$$

where $E_g(0)$ is the gap energy at 0 K, a and b are both constants related to the properties of silicon, and T_e is the absolutely effective temperature.

In summary, the new form of the photon-emission rate obtained by substituting the combination of Eq. (17) and Eq. (18) into Eq. (16) is a reasonable model of the combination of the indirect transition and direct transition that can be used to analyze the silicon light emission under breakdown condition. In regards to interpreting the optical spectrums, Akil et al. proposes a multi-mechanism model to categorize the optical spectrum into the following three sections in general [38]

- For the low photon-energy level, the mechanism is attributed to the indirect interband transitions.
- For the medium photon-energy level, the mechanism should be Bremsstrahlung radiation.
- For the high photon-energy level, direct and indirect interband electron-hole recombination may possibly be the reason.

Moreover, the indirect-to-direct conversion of optical transition in silicon materials is considered to be the dimensionality of electronic structure [3].

3. THE RELATIONSHIP BETWEEN THE ELECTRONS AND THE PHOTONS IN THE MOSFET

In the past, the method to realize a silicon light source in silicon CMOS integrated circuit relied on the following:

- Utilizing a p-n junction that operates in the reverse breakdown mode [39]; it is noted that the MOSFET device can work as two diodes (i.e., "P+ Source to N-Substrate" and "P+ Drain to N-Substrate" junctions) in parallel if the gate terminal is floated.
- Using the existing gate terminal of the MOSFET device in order to adjust the breakdown voltage BV of the two p-n junctions mentioned above [40]. Because of the linearity between the breakdown current and the optical emission power, the light intensity can be modulated by the gate terminal. The curve of the correlation between the reverse current flowing through the p-n junctions and the optical emission power as a function of the gate voltage V_g being shaped like "Z" implies that the three terminal silicon PMOSFET like light-emitting device (LED) will be a successful silicon electro-optic modulator that can be coupled to a standard mode (SM) optical fiber in order to make the establishment of on-chip optical interconnect feasible [41].
- Enhancing the light emission efficiency by means of electric field confinement and the confinement of light emitting zones close to the N-Substrate surface in close proximity to transparent Si-SiO$_2$ layers through varying the gate voltage V_g to adjust the vertical field across the gate [32, 43].

Recalling the silicon-diode LED [18–21], one of the natural defects is that the modulation of optical intensity can only be realized by adjusting the reverse bias of p-n junctions. Instead, the silicon MOSFET device with an additional terminal (gate) has the ability to modulate optical intensity directly instead of making any change of the reverse bias of the p-n junction itself. The relationship between the electrons and the photons can be obtained from the "junction breakdown current versus optical emission power" curve that is almost linear whether the silicon MOSFET device works in the mode of p-n junction diodes [32, 43] or works in the mode of p-n junction gate-controlled diodes [41, 42].

On the other hand, the relationship between electrons and photons in the MOSFET device working in the saturation region should also be investigated [44]. It is noted that the initial currents for triggering breakdown induced light emission are different for different types of operation. If the MOSFET device operates as two p-n junction diodes connected symmetrically, the initial current should be the leakage current (i.e., the impact ionization factor equals zero) of reverse-biased p-n junction; if it operates as two p-n junction gate-controlled diodes, the initial current should attributed to the tunneling current occurring in the "Gate-to-Source/Drain" overlap region underneath the gate. Compared with the two cases above, the initial current in the case of saturation mode should be due to the channel current that flows from drain terminal to the source terminal across the channel in the MOSFET device.

The photo-carrier generation mechanism is fundamentally related to the presence of hot electrons at the drain end of the scaled n-channel MOSFET (NMOSFET) device in which the drain-to-substrate is reverse-biased. Due to the increase in channel current, the drain-substrate p-n junction will reach breakdown, thereby visible light is emitted from the junction region [45]. Furthermore, the conflict between experimentally measured result and theoretically calculated result of the dependence of drain-source current I_{ds} on substrate current I_{sub} shows that there is an secondary impact ionization induced current which is believed to be attributed to the photo-induced process of electron-hole pair generation in the n-type substrate of the NMOSFET device [32]. This secondarily generated hot-electron ($SGHE$) injection current is also called the minority current observed in the substrate. It is noted that the minority current is a current that is different from the substrate current I_{sub} even if the relationship between the two types of current is almost linear.

Since I_{sub} is mainly due to the mechanism of impact ionization, the relationship between I_{sub} and I_{ds} is given by

$$I_{sub} = I_{ds} \int_0^{L_D} A_i \exp\left[-\frac{B_i}{\mathrm{E}(y)}\right] dy \tag{19}$$

where $\alpha = A_i \exp\left[-B_i/\mathrm{E}(y)\right]$ is the impact ionization rate, A_i and B_i are the ionization constants and are mainly a function of silicon material parameter itself, and L_D is the length of breakdown region near the drain-to-substrate corner. Solving Eq. (19) using a quasi two dimensional (2-D) analysis of field $E(y)$, I_{sub} can be derived from I_{ds}

$$I_{sub} = I_{ds} \left(\frac{A_i}{B_i} \right) (V_{ds} - \kappa V_{dsat}) \exp \left[-\frac{L_D B_i}{V_{ds} - \kappa V_{dsat}} \right] \qquad (20)$$

where the peak field E_m is located at $V_{ds} - \kappa V_{dsat} \approx L_D E_m$, and $0 < \kappa \leq 1$ is a technology-dependent fitting parameter and is different for standard and lightly-doped-drain (LDD) devices of MOSFET [46]. $\kappa = 1$ will make sense if L_D is equal to the effective ionization length L_e that is defined as

$$L_e = \sqrt{\left(\frac{\varepsilon_{si}}{\varepsilon_{ox}} \right) t_{ox} X_j} \qquad (21)$$

where ε_{si} is the permittivity of silicon, ε_{ox} is the permittivity of SiO$_2$ (i.e., the insulator layer in the NMOSFET device), t_{ox} is the thickness of the SiO$_2$ layer, and X_j is the junction depth of the drain/source region [47]. Substituting Eq. (21) into Eq. (20), the substrate current can be expressed as

$$I_{sub} = I_{ds} \left(\frac{A_i}{B_i} \right) (V_{ds} - V_{dsat}) \exp \left[-\frac{B_i}{V_{ds} - V_{dsat}} \sqrt{\left(\frac{\varepsilon_{si}}{\varepsilon_{ox}} \right) t_{ox} X_j} \right] \qquad (22)$$

In addition to the substrate current, the *SGHE* minority current is given by [48]

$$I_{SGHE} = C_2 \left(\frac{N_C q B_i \lambda_m}{E_g m_e A_i} \right) I_{sub} \qquad (23)$$

where N_c is the number of charged Coulomb centers per volume, λ_m is the mean-free-path, E_g is the band-gap energy, and m_e is the effective mass of electron. In addition, C_2 is a constant and q is the magnitude of elementary charge. As the first two terms are both constants, I_{SGHE} is linear with I_{sub}. Because of the linearity between the reverse current I_{sub} and the optical emission power $P_{optical}$ [49], the minority current I_{SGHE} will significantly contribute to the generation of photons in the MOSFET in the saturation region. It should be mentioned that the distribution of hot-carrier is given by Eq. (12) if the Boltzmann approximation is used. The indirect emission rate of photons in the high-field is expressed as [50]

$$R_i(hv) \infty \int_0^{hv-E_g} hvf(E)\left[1 - f(E-hv)\right]\sqrt{E\left(hv - E_g - E\right)}dE \qquad (24)$$

Substituting the function of $f(E)$ (i.e., Eq. (12)) into Eq. (24), it follows that

$$1 - f(E-hv) \approx \exp\left[-(E-hv)/(kT_e)\right] \qquad (25)$$

which implies the Bremsstrahlung radiation because of the quasi-Maxwell's distribution [32]. After correcting to account for self-absorption, Eq. (25) will arrive at the prediction of the photoemission rate constant for the measured light intensity which is Eq. (16). Combining Eq. (16), Eq. (22), Eq. (24) and Eq. (25) by jointly replacing the parameter of junction depth X_j, the photon emission intensity Φ_{photon} can be accordingly obtained as follows

$$\Phi_{photon} = C_3 I_{ds}\left(V_{ds} - V_{dsat}\right)\exp\left(-\frac{R_s L_e}{V_{ds} - V_{dsat}}\right) \qquad (26)$$

where C_3 is a constant. Recalling Eq. (19) and Eq. (20), the ratio of the substrate current I_{sub} to the channel current I_{ds} is equal to the primary impact ionization rate α, so I_{sub} is linear with I_{ds}.

On the other hand, the variation of I_{sub} with gate voltage V_g is known to exhibit a characteristic peak as shown in Figure 6. The measured light intensity Φ_{photon} is also shown in Figure 6 as a function of gate voltage V_g. The similarity between the two curves can provide the evidence of linearity between substrate current I_{sub} and light intensity Φ_{photon}. This linear relationship can also be theoretically deducted by substituting Eq. (20) into Eq. (26).

Moreover, regarding the topic of device reliability, the photon emission which is induced by hot carrier in the MOSFET device is the most direct method of probing hot-carrier phenomena and detecting device degradation in complementary metal-oxide-semiconductor integrated circuits (CMOS ICs).

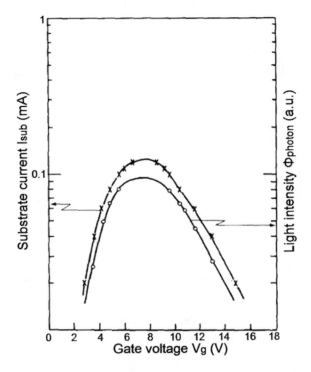

Figure 6. Substrate current I_{sub} and light intensity Φ_{photon} as a function of gate voltage V_g (After ref. [51]).

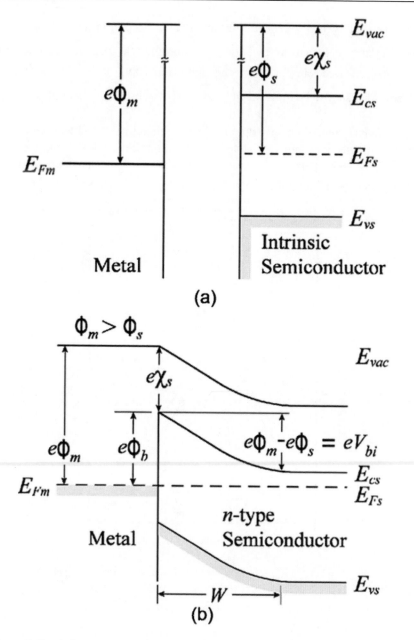

Figure 7. Band diagrams of an MOS system under (a) the flatband condition; (b) zero gate-voltage condition (After ref. [52]).

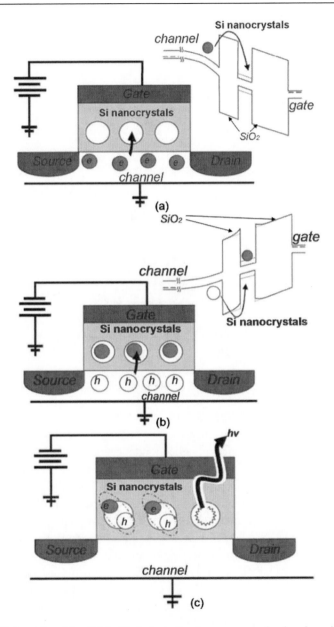

Figure 8. Schematic of the field-effect electroluminescence mechanism in a silicon nanocrystal floating-gate transistor structure: (a) electrons and subsequently; (b) by Fowler-Nordheim tunneling, and holes; (c) via Coulomb field-enhanced Fowler-Nordheim tunneling to prepare excitons that radiatively recombine (After ref. [53]).

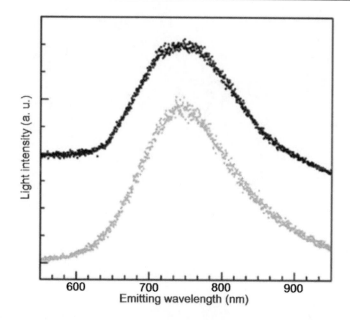

Figure 9. Emission spectra of photoluminescence (PL) and electroluminescence of the MOS-like device (After ref. [53]).

A more detailed schematic representation of the metal-oxide-semiconductor (MOS) structure is given in Figure 7 for analyzing the field-effect electroluminescence mechanism in the MOSFET device. In [53], a device based on a design very similar to the MOSFET was investigated in the aspect of electroluminescence in silicon nanocrystals. The SiO_2 thin film thermally grown on a floating gate contains a layer of Si nanocrystals prepared by ion implantation. A semitransparent polycrystalline silicon electrode is deposited at the top. If a positive voltage is applied to the gate, electrons flowing in the conductive channel between the sources S and the drain D are injected via Fowler-Nordheim tunneling to the nanocrystals, as shown in Figure 8(a). After an abrupt change of the voltage polarity, shown in Figure 8(b), holes are injected into the nanocrystals, through the Fowler-Nordheim tunneling mechanism, which is this time enhanced by Coulomb interaction. Finally, the excited nanocrystals, containing one electron-hole pair, emit luminescence photons as shown in Figure 8(c).

Accordingly, Figure 9 depicts a comparison of photoluminescence and electroluminescence spectra, confirming that the device is based on the radiative recombination taking place in silicon nanocrystals.

4. MONOLITHIC OEIC FOR ON-CHIP OPTICAL INTERCONNECTION BASED ON STANDARD CMOS TECHNOLOGY

Initiate by technical investigations in the 1940s and started as an industry in the late 1960s, CMOS technology has distinguished itself by the rapid improvement in its products [54]. In the past few decades, most of the figures of merit of the Si industry have been marked by exponential growth, principally as a result of the ability to exponentially decrease the minimum feature sizes of integrated circuits (ICs). As of today, the development of devices and processors appears to stand and possibly even overshoot Moore's law [55, 56]. Major IC technologies available for fabrication are of two types: one is Silicon Complementary Metal Oxide Semiconductor (Si-CMOS); the other is Silicon Bipolar Complementary Metal Oxide Semiconductor (Si-BiCMOS).

Si CMOS technology has been the leader in increasing of transistor density per unit area of the available silicon wafer. This scaling down of transistor size reduces the power dissipation as well as increasing the speed of the transistor. As speed increases and transistor size decreases, the breakdown voltage decreases as well as the supply voltage for the ICs. Although optimal for microprocessors and digital logic and used widely in the telecommunication and data communication areas for the logic multiplexer and de-multiplexer circuits, the scaling for higher-frequency and bit rate applications are counter to the requirement for high-voltage, high-bandwidth driver requirements.

Si-BiCMOS technology has enabled the integration of both CMOS transistor gates for monolithic digital implementation as well as bipolar transistors integrated on the same semiconductor chip. This technology makes it ideal in building monolithic solutions for driver ICs, incorporating hybrid topologies on a single silicon chip. As in the standard CMOS technology, scaling has occurred in BiCMOS technology, higher frequency of operation by decreasing transistor geometry, and decreasing supply voltages, which reduce total IC power.

On the other hand, it is becoming more apparent that development of silicon electronic IC will be limited by the rate at which data can be transmitted between devices and chips [57]. The use of copper and low k materials will allow scaling of the intermediate wiring levels, and minimize the impact on wiring delay. RC time delay, however, is dominated by global interconnect and the benefit of materials changes also is insufficient to meet overall performance requirements. Instead, optical interconnects are considered as a primary option for replacing the conductor/dielectric system for global interconnects [58], since both the speed and low power consumption requirements are believed to be solved by designing optical interconnects, Using of photons instead of electrons allows high bandwidth and high interconnection delay, while maintaining the low power consumption and high computational capability of silicon microelectronic devices. Moreover, the advantage of optical signal includes the cross-talk immunity.

CONCLUSION

The mechanism of light emission in reverse-biased silicon p-n junctions using the photon emission microscope is that of electroluminescence and this is the main focus of this chapter. Electroluminescence may be excited in a variety of ways such as through intrinsic, avalanche, tunneling and injection processes. Electroluminescence occurred at audio frequencies of the excitation field as a result of impact ionization of accelerated electrons or field emission of electrons from trapping centers is with a low efficiency, typically 1% or less [59]. For avalanche excitation, a p-n junction or a metal-semiconductor junction is reverse-biased into avalanche breakdown causing the generation of electron-hole pairs through impact ionization. Electroluminescence results through either interband (avalanche emission) or intraband (deceleration emission) transitions. In the case of tunneling injection, holes can tunnel into the valence band and subsequently recombine radiatively with electrons that have tunneled from the valence band to the conduction band across a reverse-biased semiconductor junction [60].

Overall, a wide variety of mechanisms regarding the photon generation in silicon p-n junction under avalanche breakdown condition have been fundamentally investigated. Optical integration in silicon has shown great potential because of its compatibility with microelectronics. The strongest driving force in studying optoelectronic devices arises from the need for better and more performing devices required by the modern technology society. Indeed, the progressive shrinking of the feature sizes in microelectronic devices, the increasing demand of higher clock frequencies, and the simultaneous growth in integrated circuit (IC) complexity push the traditional microelectronic devices towards their physical limits. In accordance with the International Technology Roadmap for Semiconductor (ITRS), high-performance ICs is capable of counting up to two billion transistors per chip and work with clock frequencies of the order of 10 GHz. Electrical interconnects under these conditions induce serious limitations in speed, power consumption, crosstalk, and voltages needed to bias the devices. One of the most promising solutions is to replace electrical interconnections with an optical interconnect layer. Such a solution could provide an enormous increase in bandwidth, thus eliminating any electromagnetic noise problem [18]. Since silicon electroluminescence is a powerful technique to study hot-carrier in MOSFETs and is an open research topic for silicon light sources, a new model of photon-emission rate is put forward based on the possible mechanisms of this type of optical radiation. The analysis of electroluminescence induced by the hot-carrier-effect in the MOSFET device near the "drain-substrate" high-field corner shows that the major mechanism should be attributed to the indirect transition, particularly the Bremsstrahlung radiation (i.e., indirect intraband transition). By applying this new model of photon emission rate to the MOSFET device, a new model which would provide the promising potential to predict the reliability of semiconductor device by monitoring the carrier's and photon's lifetime in the form of photon emission intensity is proposed [61].

ACKNOWLEDGMENT

I am deeply indebted to my parents who provide much-need encouragement while I am finishing the work. Finally, much is owed to my wife and son for putting up with a part-time husband and father for nearly 4 years.

REFERENCES

[1]   Pavesi, L; Guillot, G. *Optical Interconnects: The Silicon Approach*, Springer Series in Optical Sciences, 2005

[2]   Canham, L. "Silicon quantum wire array fabrication by electrochemical and chemical dissolution of wafer, *Appl. Phys. Lett.*, 57, 10, 1046-1048, 1990

[3] Kanemitsu, Y; Suzuki, K; Kyushin, S; Matsumoto, H. "Visible photoluminescence from silicon-backbone polymers," *Phys. Rev. B*, vol. 51, no. 19, 13103-13110, 1995

[4] Schmuki, P; Erickson, L; Lockwood, D. "Light emitting micropatterns of porous Si created at surface defects," *Phys. Rev. Lett.*, vol. 80, no. 18, 4060-4063, 1998

[5] Franzo, G; Priolo, F; Coffa, S; Polman, A; Carnera, A. "Room-temperature electroluminescence from Er-doped crystalline Si," *Appl. Phys. Lett.*, vol. 64, iss. 17, 2235-2237, 1994

[6] Brehm, M ; Suzuki, T; Fromhertz, T; Zhong, Z; Hrauda, N; Hackl, F; Stangl, J; Schäffler, F; Bauer, G. "Combined structural and photoluminescence study of SiGe islands on Si substrates: comparison with realistic energy level calculations," *New J. of Phys.*, 11, 063021, 2009

[7] Lynch, S. "Intersubband electroluminescence from Si/SiGe cascade emitter at terahertz frequencies," *Appl. Phys. Lett.*, vol. 81, no. 9, 1543-1545, 2002

[8] Dehlinger, G; Diehl, L; Gennser, U; Sigg, H; Faist, J; Ensslin, K; Grützmacher, D; Müller, E. "Intersubband electroluminescence from silicon-based quantum cascade structures," *Science*, vol. 290, no. 5500, 2277-2280, 2000

[9] Sun, X; Liu, J; Kimerling, L; Michel, J. "Direct gap photoluminescence of n-type tensile-strained Ge-on-Si," *Appl. Phys. Lett.*, 95, 011911, 2009

[10] Castagna, M; Coffa, S; Monaco, M; Caristia, L; Messina, A; Mangano, R; Bongiorno, C. "Si-based materials and devices for light emission in silicon," *Physica E*, vol. 16, iss. 3-4, 547-553, 2003

[11] Rong, H; Jones, R; Liu, A; Cohen, O; Hak, D; Fang, A; Paniccia, M. "A continuous-wave raman silicon laser," *Nature*, 433, 725-728, 2005

[12] Boyraz, O; Jalali, B. "Demonstration of a silicon Raman laser," *Opt. Exp.*, vol. 12, iss. 21, 5269-5273, 2004

[13] Fang, A; Park, H; Kuo, Y; Jones, R; Cohen, O; Liang, D; Raday, O; Sysak, M; Paniccia, M; Bowers, J. "Hybrid silicon evanescent devices," *Materials Today*, vol. 10, no. 7-8, 28-35, 2007

[14] Wang, Y; Chen, W; Liao, X; Cao, Z. "Amorphous silicon nanoparticles in compound films grown on cold substrates for high-efficiency photoluminescence," *Nanotechnology*, vol. 14, no. 11, 1235-1238, 2003

[15] Newman, R. "Visible light from a silicon p-n junction," *Phys. Rev.* 100, 700–703, 1955

[16] Rose, D. "Microplasma in silicon," *Phys. Rev.*, vol. 105, iss. 2, 413-418, 1957

[17] Lacaita, A; Zappa, F; Bigliardi, S; Manfredi, M. "On the bremsstrahlung origin of hot-carrier-induced photons in silicon devices," *IEEE Trans. Electron. Dev.*, vol. 40, no. 3, 577-582, 1993

[18] Huang, B; Zhang, X; Wang, W; Dong, Z; Guan, N; Zhang, Z; Chen, H. "CMOS monolithic optoelectronic integrated circuit for on-chip optical interconnection," *Opt. Commun.*, vol. 284, iss. 16-17, 3924-3927, 2011

[19] Morschbach, M; Oehme, M; Kasper, E. "Visible light emission by a reverse-biased integrated silicon diode," *IEEE Trans. Electron. Dev.*, vol. 54, no. 5, 1091-1094, 2007

[20] Kramer, J; Seitz, P; Steigmeier, E; Auderset, H; Delley, B. "Light-emitting devices in industrial CMOS technology", 527-533, vol. 37-38, *Sens. Actuators A*, vol. 37-38, 527-533, 1993

[21] Snyman, L; Plessis, M; Aharoni, H. "Injection-avalanche based n^+pn Si CMOS LED's (450nm-750nm) with two order increase in light emission intensity – Application for next generation silicon-based optoelectronics," *Jpn. J. Appl. Physics*, 46, 2474-2480, 2007

[22] Campbell, S. *The Science and Engineering of Microelectronic Fabrication*, New York: Oxford University Press, 1996

[23] Chynoweth, A; Mckay, H. "Photon emission from avalanche breakdown in silicon," *Phys. Rev.*, vol. 102, iss. 2, 369-376, 1956

[24] Akil, N; Houtsma, V; Le Minh, P; Holleman, J; Zieren, V; de Mooij, D; Woerlee, P; van den Berg, A; Wallinga, H. "Modeling of light-emission spectra measured on silicon nanometer-scale diode antifuses," *J. Appl. Phys.*, vol. 88, iss. 4, 1916-2480, 2007

[25] Haecker, W. "Infared radiation from breakdown plasmas in Si, Gasb, and Ge: Evidence for direct free hole radiation," *Phys. Status Solidi (a)*, vol. 25, iss. 1, 301-310, 1974

[26] Obeidat, A; Kalayjian, Z; Andreou, A; Khurgin, J. "A model for visible photon emission from reverse-biased silicon p-n junctions," *Appl. Phys. Lett.*, 70, 470, 1997

[27] Bude, J; Sano, N; Yoshii, A. "Hot-carrier luminescence in Si," *Phys. Rev. B*, vol. 45, no. 11, 5848-5856, 1992

[28] Willardson, R; Beer, A. *Semiconductors and Semimetals*, vol. 8, p. 245, 1972

[29] Gautam, D; Khokle, W; Garg, K. "Photon emission from reverse-biased silicon P-N junctions," *Solid State Electron.*, vol. 31, no. 2, 219-222, 1988

[30] Ono, K; Tarucha, S. "Nuclear-spin-induced oscillatory current in spin-blockaded quantum dots," *Phys. Rev. Lett.*, vol. 92, iss. 25, 256803, 2004

[31] Wolff, P. "Theory of optical radiation from breakdown avalanches in germanium," *J. Phys. Chem. Solids.*, vol. 16, iss. 3-4, 184-190, 1960

[32] Xu, K; Li, G. "A novel way to improve the quantum efficiency of silicon light-emitting diode in a standard silicon complementary metal-oxide-semiconductor technology," *J. Appl. Phys.*, 113, 10, 103106, 2013

[33] Yamashita, J; Inoue, K. "Hot electron in n-type germanium," *J. Phys. Chem. Solids.*, vol. 12, iss. 1, 1-21, 1959

[34] Shewchun, J; Wei, L. "Mechanism for reverse-biased breakdown radiation in p–n junctions," *Solid-State Electron.*, vol. 8, no. 5, 485-493, 1965

[35] Lahbabi, M; Ahaitouf, A; Abarkan, E; Fliyou, M; Hoffmann, A; Charles, J; Bhuva, B; Kerns, S; Kerns Jr., D. "Analyses of electroluminescence spectra of silicon junctions in avalanche breakdown using an indirect interband recombination model," *Appl. Phys. Lett.*, 70, 20, 3182-3184, 2000

[36] Elghazi, H; Jorio, A; Zorkani, I. "Analysis of silicon light emission under breakdown condition using an indirect intraband model," *Opt. Commun.*, vol. 281, iss. 12, 3320-3323, 2008

[37] Aspnes, D; Studna, A. "Dielectric functions and optical parameters of Si, Ge, GaP, GaAs, GaSb, InP, InAs, and InSb from 1.5 to 6.0 eV," *Phys. Rev. B*, 27, 2, 985-1009, 1983

[38] Akil, N; Kerns, S; Kerns Jr., D; Hoffmann, A; Charles, J. "A multimechanism model for photon generation by silicon junctions in avalanche breakdown," *IEEE Trans. Electron. Dev.*, vol. 46, no. 5, 1022-1028, 1999

[39] Xu, K; Li, G. "A light-emitting-device (LED) with monolithic integration on bulk silicon in a standard CMOS technology," in *International Photonics and Optoelectronics Meetings (POEM)*, OSA Technical Digest, 2013

[40] Xu, K; Li, G. "Silicon electro-optic modulator based on the theory of gate-controlled diode," in *International Photonics and Optoelectronics Meetings (POEM)*, OSA Technical Digest, 2013

[41] Xu, K; Li, G. "A three terminal silicon-PMOSFET like light-emitting device (LED) for optical intensity modulation," *IEEE Photonics J.*, vol. 4, no. 6, 2159-2168, 2012

[42] Xu, K. "Current-voltage characteristics and increase in the quantum efficiency of three-terminal gate and avalanche-based Si LEDs," *Appl. Opt.*, 52, 27, 6669-6675, 2013

[43] Xu, K; Li, G. "Light-emitting device with monolithic integration on bulk silicon in standard complementary metal oxide semiconductor technology," *J. Nanophoton.*, 7, 073082, 2013

[44] Xu, K; Li, G. "Hot-carrier induced photon-emission in silicon metal-oxide-semiconductor field-effect-transistor," *J. Phys.: Conf. Ser.: XXXVIII International Conference on Photonics, Electronics and Atomic Collision, (ICPEAC 2013)*, 2013

[45] Tam, S; Hsu, F; Ko, P; Hu, C; Muller, R. "Spatially resolved observation of visible-light emission from Si MOSFET's," *IEEE Electron Dev. Lett.*, vol. 4, no. 10, 386-388, 1983

[46] Arora, N; Sharma, M. "MOSFET substrate current model for circuit simulation," *IEEE Trans. Electron. Dev.*, vol. 38, no. 6, 1392-1398, 1991

[47] Tam, S; Ko, P; Hu, C; Muller, R. "Correlation between substrate and gate currents in MOSFET's," *IEEE Trans. Electron. Dev.*, vol. 29, no. 11, 1740-1744, 1982

[48] Tam, S; Hu, C. "Hot-electron-induced photon and photocarrier generation in Silicon MOSFET's," *IEEE Trans. Electron. Dev.*, vol. 31, no. 9, 1264- 1273, 1984

[49] Toriumi, A; Yoshimi, M; Iwase, M; Akiyama, Y; Taniguchi, K. "A study of photon emission from n-channel MOSFET's," *IEEE Trans. Electron. Dev.*, vol. 34, no. 7, 1501-1508, 1987

[50] Yamada, S; Kitao, M. "Recombination radiation as possible mechanism of light emission from reverse-biased p-n junctions under breakdown conditions," *Jpn. J. Appl. Phys.*, vol. 32, iss. 10R, 4555-4559, 1993

[51] Childs, P; Stuart, R; Eccleston, W. "Evidence of optical generation of minority carriers from saturated MOS transistors," *Solid-State Electron.*, vol. 26, no. 7, 685–688, 1983

[52] Taur, Y; Ning, T. *Fundamentals of Modern VLSI Devices*, 2nd ed, Cambridge University Press, New York, 2009

[53] Walters, R; Bourianoff, G; Atwater, H. "Field-effect electroluminescence in silicon nanocrystals," *Nature Materials*, vol. 4, 143-146, 2005

[54] Moore, G. "Progress in digital integrated electronics," in *IEEE Int. Electron Devices Meeting (IEDM) Tech. Dig.*, 1975, 11-13

[55] Meindl, J; Chen, Q; Davis, J. "Limits on silicon nanoelectronics for terascale integration," *Science*, vol. 293, no. 5537, 2044-2049, 2001

[56] Meindl, J. "Beyond Moore's law: the interconnect era," *Computing in Science and Engineering*, vol. 5, iss. 1, 20-24, Jan/Feb 2003

[57] Theis, T. "The future of interconnection technology," *IBM J. Res. Develop.*, vol. 44, no. 3, p. 379, 2000

[58] Miller, D. "Rationale and challenge for optical interconnects to electronic chips," *Proc. of IEEE*, vol. 88, iss. 6, 728-749, 2000

[59] Xu, K. "On the design and optimization of three-terminal light-emitting device in silicon CMOS technology," *IEEE J. of Select. Topics Quantum Electron.*, vol. 20. no. 4, 8201208, 2014

[60] Xu, K; Li, G. "The path forward: silicon electro-optical interface for modern complementary metal-oxide-semiconductor integrated circuits (CMOS ICs)," in *2nd CIOMP-OSA Summer Session,* OSA Technical Digest (online) (Optical Society of America, 2013)

[61] Selmi, L; Pavesi, M; Wong, H; Acovic, A; Sangiorgi, E. "Monitoring hot-carrier degradation in SOI MOSFET's by hot-carrier luminescence techniques," *IEEE Trans. Electron. Dev.*, vol. 45, no. 5, 1135-1139, 1998

In: Advances in Optoelectronics Research   ISBN: 978-1-63321-211-4
Editor: Marcus R. Oswald   © 2014 Nova Science Publishers, Inc.

Chapter 2

SUPRAMOLECULAR POLYMER SEMICONDUCTORS (SPSS) TOWARD ORGANIC MECHATRONICS

Ling-Hai Xie[1,] and Wei Huang[1,2,†]*
[1]Center for Molecular Systems and Organic Devices (CMSOD),
Key Laboratory for Organic Electronics & Information Displays
(KLOEID) and Institute of Advanced Materials (IAM),
Nanjing University of Posts and Telecommunications (NUPT),
Nanjing, China
[2]Jiangsu-Singapore Joint Research Center for Organic/Bio- Electronics &
Information Displays and Institute of Advanced Materials,
Nanjing Tech. University, Nanjing, China

ABSTRACT

Controllable noncovalent forces drive organic/polymer semiconductors into supramolecular organic devices with distinguishing functional features. Supramolecular polymer semiconductors (SPSs) have not only extraordinary optoelectronic characters, but also potentially self-assembly, soft and mechanical features, self-healing and stimuli-responsive behaviors. In this chapter, we explored a series of supramolecular approaches to plastic electronics and demonstrated the

* Email: iamlhxie@njupt.edu.cn.
† Email: iamwhuang@njupt.edu.cn.

supramolecular resistive switching and supramolecular electro-luminescence. Firstly, π-stacked polymer semiconductors exhibit two supramolecular features: the reversible conformational change and the behaviors of molecular tweezers. Hindrance-functionalized stacked polymers were explored to apply for host materials in polymer light-emitting devices (PLEDs) and resistive switching materials in polymer nonvolatile flash memory. Secondly, we found the polyfluorene gels in 1,2-dichloroethane (DCE) at room temperatures with the feature emission peak at ~476 nm. Polyfluorenol-based supramolecular conjugated polymers (SCPs) exhibit the strong molecular assembled ability into gels, nanoparticles (nanogels) and aggregate bulk homojunction thin-films. Rather than ketone defect, aggregate mechanism of g-band at ~530 nm in PLEDs were supported by strong green emission of polyfluorenol-based SCPs in solution. PPFOH exhibit the color-tunable supramolecular (electro)luminescence in solutions, thin films and devices, ranging from blue, green, yellow, orange to white color by changing the molecular weight and formula solvents. We believe that SPSs and supramolecular mechatronics will become the cornerstone of organic learning mechano-devices to activate molecular consciousness toward organic intelligence robotics that will make one powerful science solution to social society in the 21st century.

Keyword: Organic semiconductors, noncovalent forces, supramolecular approaches, electroluminescence, resistive memory

INTRODUCTION

After the silicon, carbon element become an alternative to (opto)electronics for information, energy and control technology. Organic devices have several advantages such as low-cost fabrication, large area, excellent mechanical endurance, designability by molecular engineering and molecular scale size ultimately over counterpart inorganic semiconductor devices [1-3]. On the one hand, organic devices become attractive since the high-efficiency bilayer organic light-emitting devices (OLEDs) was reported by Tang et al. in 1987 [4]. One the other hand, polymer devices have been extensively investigated by the discovery of the high conductivity of polyacetylene in 1977 by Heeger et al. [5] and the first polymer light-emitting devices (PLEDs) in 1990 by Friend et al. [6]. After this, various organic/polymer devices such as O/PLEDs, organic photovoltaics (OPV), organic/polymer field-effect transistors (OFET), organic/polymer nonvolatile memories, organic lasers and photodectors have been reported continuously. [2, 7-10] The last two decades have witnessed the rapid progress in organic/plastic electronics that enough deliver a massage of carbon element in periodic table that will be potential and effective for the component of semiconductors and optoelectronic materials in 21th century. After the significantly improved luminescence and mobility, OLED technique for flat panel display and solid light sources have been commercialized by the joining efforts between science and industry. The ever doubt on device performance and stability have been excluded gradually. Recently, AMOLED have been extensively applied to serve as mobile phones by Samsung. However, from the long term point of view, compared to time and energy-consumptive vacuum thermal evaporation (VTE) deposition, low-cost, high throughput and eco-friendly solution-processed chemical fabrication and film-forming deposition become emerging technique to organic/plastic electronics.

Besides other factors, one major progress in this area is ascribed to molecular design of organic/ polymer semiconductors. Top-down molecular design created various RGB and white light-emitting materials for PLEDs, high- mobility materials for OFET, and wide-absorption p-n (donor-acceptor) materials for OPV. [3, 11] Now, it is more and clearer for the design principle of organic semiconductors in terms of electronic structures via the covalent synthesis. However, the wet chemical fabrication is more uncontrollable and unrepeatable in terms of thin films. All functional molecular systems are dominated by the ubiquitous noncovalent forces, including the pi-pi interaction, van der Waals' force, hydrogen bond, dipole-dipole interaction, coordinative bond and other. An impressive example is DNA that can be called as the king of molecules with smart behaviors and excellent features in a suitable external environment thanks to the subtle arrangement of helix polymer chains and the synergic drive forces of pi-pi staking and hydrogen bonding. Supramolecular approaches become the potential tools to update organic devices in terms of the material design, interface, film procedure, and device structure. [12-13] The concept of supramolecular electronics has been proposed to create aggregate-based nanodevices that become an alternative to molecular electronics and nanoelectronics. [14-19] More and more evidence have supported that the secondary interchain interactions in supramolecular polymers are of utmost importance to charge carriers and excitons [20-27], fluorescence resonance energy transfer (FRET) [28], thin film morphology [29-32], device performance [33], repeatable film procedures, and ink formula as well as the functional extension. [34-36] As a result, supramolecular approaches offer an powerful alternative to morphologies-directed molecular design [37-39].

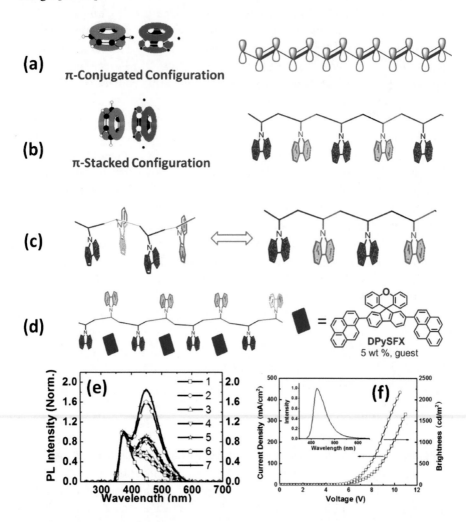

Figure 1. (a, b) two basic electronic charge channels in polymer semiconductors: π-conjugated and π-stacked motifs that corresponds to π-conjugated polymers and stacked polymers, (c, d) three conformation chains in stacked polymers, (e, f) photoluminescence of PVK in solution and electroluminescence of DPySFX doped in PVK.

Supramolecular approach to polymer electronics will make thin-film devices more effective, repeatable and smart in consideration of the robust joining advantages of soft and mechanical feature of polymers, optoelectronic properties of semiconductors, and the assemble behaviors of supramolecular systems [40-43]. It is expected that the new-generation as-called supramolecular polymer semiconductors (SPSs) could be created when the semiconducting features and supramolecular essences are combined into one polymer chain via covalent molecular engineering. SPSs with both excellent optoelectronic properties and potential self-assembly behaviors probably become one powerful kind of advanced materials to solve the issues in plastic electronics and optoelectronics. Furthermore, supramolecular physics should be the intrinsic progress in condensed matter physics from organic inks to films and the law of aggregate behaviors via driving non-covalent forces after soft condensed matter physics, molecular physics and solid-state physics. In this chapter, we focus on our works of SPSs in plastic electronics. One is stacked polymers with intrinsic SPS feature of reversible conformational change and molecular tweezers that have been explored for the application of polymer hosts in polymer light-emitting devices (PLEDs) and electrically bistable polymers in organic nonvolatile memories. The other is sidechain-type supramolecular conjugated polymers (SCPs) that have been synthesized by supramolecular functionalization of conjugated polymers to understand the morphology, aggregates and luminescence in PLEDs. Polyfluorenol-based SCPs exhibited excellent the capability of molecular assembly to achieve supramolecular conjugated polymer gels, nanoparticles and nanogels. The introduction of hydrogen bonding make polyfluorenes strong green emission band (g-band) in solution that afford robust evidence on the aggregate mechanism in polyfluorene-based PLEDs. Polyfluorenol-based SCPs exhibits the feature of supramolecular luminescence with the large molecular weight and solvent effects. Color tunable supramolecular electroluminescence has been established by host-guest aggregate homojunction thin films. Finally, the future roadmap of SPSs has been perspective. Supramolecular thin-film electronics, supramolecular optoelectronics, supramolecular spintronics and supramolecular mechatronics will make a powerful science solution to social society in the 21 century that is coined as an era of consciousness [2].

Stacked Polymer Semiconductors

Organic semiconductors have the nature of pi- semiconductors (Figure 1a). In all supramolecular non-covalent interactions, the pi-pi interactions are extraordinary importance for organic semiconductors because they are molecular condensed solids with pi-orbital carrier-transporting channels [37]. Many results have been suggested the intermolecular stacking modes that dramatically change the electronic transport and exciton behaviors [44]. Therefore, to create the supramolecular π-channels will afford effective platform to active potential molecular optoelectronic functions [45-46]. The pi-pi interactions as one non-covalent force have the typical bonding energy of 8–12 kJ/mol in supramolecular chemistry. There are three basic patterns, including face-to-face stacking, parallel-displaced stacking, and T-shaped stacking. The aromatic plane can be either planar or curve one [47] Up to date, there are two extreme channel configurations that are pi-conjugated motifs and pi-stacked motifs, respectively. As a result, pi-stacked molecules and polymers are cross nodes between supramolecular chemistry and organic/polymer electronics. Stacked polymers become one molecular design of the supramolecular conductive channels where electrons or charge carriers can mobile and drift via the hoping modes. In fact, state-of-the-art stacked channels exist in bimolecular DNA [48-55] that belongs to one kind of SPS. Another kind of artificial stacked polymers is the poly(N-vinylcarbozale) (PVK) that have been employed as a model of supramolecular organic semiconductors (Figure 1b) [56]. PVK can be regarded as the polyethylene chains with pendent intrachain noncovalent pi-pi stacked tubes (Figure 3). PVK was first synthesized by 1934 and served as the excellent photoconductive and photorefractive materials [57]. In O/PLED, PVK often serve as the hole transport materials with a HOMO of ~-5.4 eV, relative ITO electrode with a work function of ~4.7 eV. There are two key supramolecular features for PVK in solution and organic devices. One is the stimuli-responsive conformational change under special external conditions as shown in Figure 4a. In fact, the switching transition of polymer chain in dilute solution can be characterized by the photoluminescence spectra as shown in Figure 1e. There are two broad emission peaks in PVK solution: one is ~380 nm from partially eclipsed stacks, the other is ~ 420 nm from face-to-face stacks [58]. We found the second peak at 420 nm increase with the increased number of scanning [26], suggesting the arrangement from partially stacking to face-to-face stacking under the driving force of radical ions. The observation inspired us to make advance electrically memorable polymers for nonvolatile memory devices and information storages [56], although the big gap and difference between solutions, thin films and devices should be considered toward this targets as shown in the next section. The other supramolecular feature of PVK-based stacked polymers is the function of molecular tweezers with swallowing capability of guests by means of the unique conformation as shown in Figure 1d. This tweezer conformation serve as blending hosts of pyrenes in PLEDs [59]. The device with a configuration of ITO/ PEDOT:PSS (40 nm)/ DPSFX (5 wt %): PVK (80 nm)/CsF (2 nm)/Al (90 nm) exhibit the deep blue emission with a Internationale de l'Eclairage (CIE) coordinate of (0.16, 0.08), turn-on voltage of 4.3 V, maximum luminance of 2000 cd/m^2, luminous efficiency of 1.1 cd/A [60]. Electroluminescence (EL) spectra of devices are similar to that of DPySFX in dilute solution that suggest pyrenes are single-molecule dispersion in PVK matrix, otherwise the large red-shift that should occur owing to the intermolecular stacking aggregates. The preliminary observation encourage us exploring supramolecular polymer host-guest systems. Up to date, there are three key conformation states that can modulate the electron or exciton behaviors in stacked polymers.

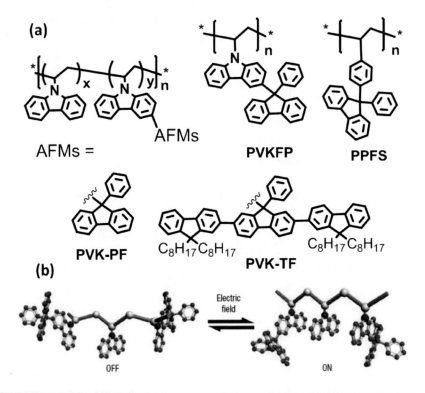

Figure 2. (a) Hindrance-functionalized pi-stacked polymer semiconductors and (b) a possible schematic mechanism of supramolecular resistive switching.

Hindrance-Functionalized pi-Stacked Polymer Semiconductors

From the molecular structure point of view, one polymer chain is dominated generally by electronic structures, steric hindrances, conformation and topology as well as supramolecular motifs according to the four-element principle [37]. In the background, we demonstrated the hindrance functionalization strategies of supramolecular stacked polymers using the bulky arylfluorene moieties (AFMs) via the Friedel-Crafts post-modification and direct polymerization. Three PVK derivatives that are PVK-PF, PVPFK, and PVK-TF, and a polystyrene-based PPFS have been prepared as shown in Figure 2a. Preliminary characterization showed hindrance functionalization can make better thermal, morphological, electrochemical and photo stability than that of precursor PVK. PVPFK has high decomposition temperature (T_d) of up to 434 °C and no glass phase transition [61]. 9-phenylfluorene moieties (PFMs) can slightly improve electron transporting ability of PVPFK with a LUMO energy level of -2.08 eV in comparison with PVK with a LUMO energy level of -1.90 eV. Furthermore, a prototype PLED of PVK-TF with a device configuration of ITO/PEDOT:PSS/PVK-TF/Ca/Ag exhibit outstanding stable deep-blue emission with a CIE coordinate of (0.20, 0.10) and a width at half maximum (FWHM) of ~60 nm at 100 mA/cm^2 (35 V). [62]

Supramolecular Resistive Switching

Organic nonvolatile resistive memories become emerging alternative technology to information storage at the era of big data by means of their bottom-up low-cost fabrication, 3-dimensional high-density stacking architectures and potential wearable features [63]. There are three basic memory types, including volatile dynamic random-access memory (DRAM) and static random-access memory (SRAM), nonvolatile write-once-read-many-times (WORM) memory, and rewritable/erasable flash memory device. The latter is emerging. Inorganic memory are able to achieve resistive switching by either filamentary mechanism or phase change. Similarly, conformational change is one possible strategy to achieve polymer nonvolatile flash memory that are still unachievable. Bulky hindrance with steric repulsion can serve as tools to manipulate the behaviors of conformations by balancing supramolecular attraction without obvious change of electronic structures [64].

Table 1. Device performances based on stacked polymer host materials

host	dopant (contents [%])	V_{on} [a] [V]	L_{max} [cd/m^2]	$L.E._{max}$ [cd/A]	$P.E._{max}$ [lm/W]	$L.E.$ [b] [cd/A]	$P.E.$ [b] [lm/W]	$L.E.$ [c] [cd/A]	$P.E.$ [c] [lm/W]	CIE [x, y]
PVK	FIrpic (30%)	7.4	10968	13.3	2.4	6.1	1.5	12.9	2.2	0.16, 0.40
PVPFK	FIrpic (30%)	6.1	13287	14.2	2.8	12.0	2.7	14.1	2.6	0.15, 0.38
PVK-TF	Ir(BT)2(acac) (2%)	5.8	18595	22.0	10.5	21.6	10.4	18.8	7.7	0.47, 0.48
PVK-TF	Ir(BT)2(acac) (0.1%)	5.0	15723	10.7	4.8	10.6	4.6	8.6	2.9	0.38, 0.39

[a] Recorded at 1 cd/m^2.
[b] Measured at a brightness of 100 cd/m^2. [c] Measured at a brightness of 1000 cd/m^2.

We make attempt to investigate a series of supramolecular memory devices using hindrance-functionalized stacked polymers such as PPFS [65] and PVK-PFs [57]. PVK-PF-based supramolecular electronic devices was fabricated with a sandwiched configuration of ITO/PVK-PF/Al. Organic devices exhibited a SET process (or a 'writing' process) with a low transition voltage of 2.2 V and a RESET process (or a 'erasing' process) with a reverse voltage at -2.0 V, suggesting that it belong to nonvolatile flash memory devices. Device show the on/off ratio of 10^4 and the conductivity current of ON/ OFF states are 10^{-7} and 10^{-11} A, respectively. PVK-PF-based supramolecular memory devices were able to tolerate 10^8 read cycles in the ON/OFF states, 6 hours of continuous stress tests at 1 V, as well as hundreds of the writing/erasing processes. The simulation of I-V characteristics exhibit the high resistance state with a space-charge limited current (SCLC) and the low resistance state with a thermionic emission current. A rational scenario of supramolecular resistance switching have proposed as shown in Figure 2b. The eclipsed stacking motifs corresponds to the low-conductivity state and the face-to-face stacking to the high-conductivity state. It should be noted that the detailed mechanism is more complicated than we thought that are waiting for examination by molecular scale device experiments and theoretical calculation, although some experiments have been done with the aim to rule out the filamentary conduction effect, for example, the ON-state current increased with the raising temperature and the linear dependence of current magnitude on the active device area. Nevertheless, we demonstrated one state-of-the-art approach to achieve the conformational change for polymer flash memory devices that were only demonstrated using covalent closure-opening of Rose Bengal small molecules by Pal et al. in 2004. [66] Our result exhibited that PVK-based stacked polymers exhibit more capability to design the electrically memorable polymers than any other nonconjugated polymers with pendent active segments. [67, 68] The steric effects to tune the charge transport of polymer optoelectronic materials become one promising platform for other device application. Supramolecular resistors will open one door to smart nonlinear devices by means of the integration of electronic and mechano functional segments into one molecule or polymers.

Supramolecular Electrophosphorescent Polymer Host Materials

Stacked polymers possess not only the unique phase transition of conformational change for resistive flash memories, but also can serve as the supramolecular electrophosphorescent host materials with a advantage of high triplet energy levels over conjugated polymers and conjugation-interrupted polymers. Beside the tweezer conformation that can take up the guest of metal complex to form the supramolecular host-guest systems, stacked polymers are considered to be one unique polymer host materials for blue light emitting electro-phosphorescence in PLEDs. If the tweezer conformation could take up guests effectively, single-molecule dispersion probably make them purified emission color and reduce the quenching effects. In this background, we demonstrated PVFPK-based stacked polymers as supramolecular electrophosphorescent host materials (Table 1). PVPFK has a phosphorescent peak at 442 nm, corresponding to a triplet energy level of 2.80 eV, slightly lower than that of PVK (E_T =2.95 eV, 422 nm). We choice a blue guest of the bis[(4,6-difluorophenyl)pyridinato-N,C^2(picolinato) iridium(III) (FIrpic) with a E_T of 2.65 eV to fabricate the host-guest electro-phosphorescent PLED with the configuration of ITO/PEDOT:PSS (10 nm)/host: 30% FIrpic(65 nm)/TPBI (40 nm)/Ca:Ag. From the device performance, PVPFK devices exhibited the luminescence efficiency (L. E.) and power efficiency (P. E.) higher than that of PVK and the stability over PVK-based counterparts. The brightness of PVPFK device reached up to 12418 cd/m^2 at 17 V. PVFPK-based devices have the turn-on voltage of 6.1 V lower than that of PVK (7.4 V) at a brightness of 1 cd/m^2. The lower turn-on voltage contributed to the reduction of LUMO after the introduction of PFMs into PVPFK. The EL spectra with a narrower emission profile indicated that the guest of FIrpic molecules can disperse more uniformed in PVK-PF than that in precursor PVK. PVPFK-based devices have a CIE coordinate of (0.15, 0.38) with a fwhm of 60.9 nm and a CIE coordinate of (0.16, 0.40) with a fwhm of 65.5 nm for PVK-based devices. [61]. Different from the PVK-PF, PVK-TF is a typical double-channel multifunctional system with both π-stacked and conjugated chains. It can be expected that on the one hand, PVK with stacked channels serve as the function of hole transporting, on the other hand, the oligofluorenes with conjugated channels serve as the function of blue light emission. This stack-conjugation integration afford a method to reduce the number of host-guest white devices from three components to single guest. In consideration of a triplet energy of 2.28 eV, we demonstrated the PVK-TF as multifunctional host materials for white electrophosphorescent devices using a dopant of orange phosphor, bis(2-phenylbenzothiazolato) (acetylacetonate)iridium(III) (Ir(BT)2(acac)), with a triplet energy level of 2.23 eV. [69]

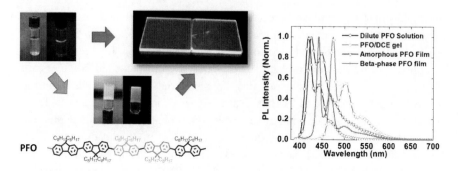

Figure 3. The basic relation among solution, gel, and thin films, the chemical structures of poly(9,9-dioctyl fluorene) (PFO) and its photoluminescence in various states.

The devices with configuration of ITO/PEDOT:PSS/ PVK-TF: Ir(BT)2(acac) /TPBi /Ag(Ca) using 5% dopant exhibit the highly stable efficient orange phosphorescent PLEDs with maximum luminance of 19552.3 cd/m^2 and maximum efficiency of up to 21.99 cd/A, comparable with some thermal deposited multilayer devices. When the content of dopant reduce to 0.1% at the same device configuration, the white emission with high colour-rendering index (CRI) of 81.9 and correlated color temperature (CCT) of 3774 that are better than all reported white PLEDs based on two components complementary emitters of blue fluorescent materials and orange phosphor that always exhibit low CRI of 50~70. If the electronic transport layers using a triazine derivative, 2,4,6-tri(biphenyl-3-yl)-1,3,5-triazine, our supramolecular white PLEDs keep the high CRI of 81.7 with high brightness of 15723.3 cd/m^2 as well as acceptable efficiency of 10.69 cd/A, making it among high performance white PLEDs. Our result suggested that to integrate π-stacked and conjugated polymers open a bright door to rational molecular design single-polymer supramolecular light-emitting host materials for high-performance PLEDs. DNA is the smartest molecules and polymers with various fascinating features, such as molecular recognition, molecular assembly, and others. Stacked polymers that could be called as artificial DNA will make organic/polymer semiconductors more smart to manipulate the electron charge and exciton as well as condensed behaviors for the extraordinary multifunctional devices.

Polyfluorene-Based Supramolecular Gels and Aggregate Luminescence

Solution-processable organic (opto)electronics will be a next-generation solution to information display and storage technology. However, their device performances are not only dependent on the electronic structures, but also strongly on the thin film morphology. It is emerging to clarify that the molecular condensation from solution to thin films. Physical gels are intermediate between solution and solids that offer an excellent model to understand the condensation and aggregation of organic optical inks into thin films by wet chemical low-cost fabrications such as printed procedures [70]. Physical reversible sol-gel processes benefit for the understanding intermolecular interactions and morphology evolution of solvents at the noncovalent level. In this background, we demonstrate the solvent effects of organic optical solutions on gelation and thin morphology as well as their photophysics. We found the existence of precursor superstructures in solution or sol by examining the difference from UV-vis electronic absorption and photoluminescence spectra in both gelation and nongelation solvents. For example, PFO have polymorphism phenomena, several phases such as amorphous phase, beta-phase, γ-phase in crystals, liquid crystalline, and others. Until now, the PFO can aggregate into gel at limited kinds of solvents, one is toluene at -20 °C and the other is 1,2-dichloroethane (DCE) that have been discovery by our group [70]. When thin film of PFO was fabricated by spin coating technique from the toluene, the PL spectra exhibit the feature of amorphous state with 0-0, 0-1, and 0-2 intrachain singlet transition of 419, 443, and 472 nm. Some processes can make the formation of beta phased with the 0-0 transition at the peak of ~446 nm. In fact, if you examine PFO/DCE gel, you can find the content of beta phase more than 50% from the UV and the first 0-0 transition at ~476 nm in fluorescence spectra (Figure 3). The result suggests that the high-ordered superstructure exist in physical networking by noncovalent forces, including columns aggregates that have been characterized by small angle X-ray scattering (SAXS). When the films have been fabricated by DCE, the PL spectra have obvious beta-phase emission. The fact suggests that superstructure with the feature peak at 476 nm could collapse by spin coating forces that probably are equivalent to supramolecular forces. The other is gelation solvent make beta phase easier than other solvents. PLEDs based on β-phase thin films spin coated from DCE exhibits current efficiency of up to 3.43 cd/A that is 3.7 times higher than that of the device from amorphous phase. [71]

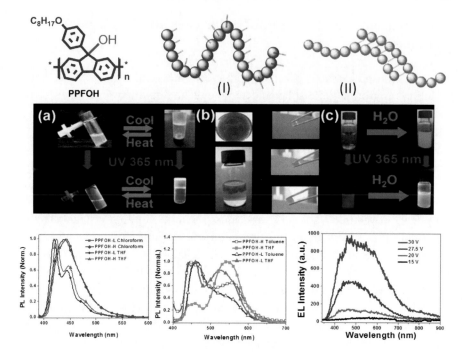

Figure 4. Chemical structure of PPFOH, basic two type of chain architectures of PPFOHs, its gels, nano- or macro-suspension, fluorescence spectra in dilute solvents, spin-coating thin films and electroluminescence of nanoparticles.

Furthermore, the device with β-phase emission has obvious advantages such as stable emission and high color purity over amorphous-phase devices. The result agree with reports from other groups on the beta phase with various advantages in terms of high mobility, low turn-on voltage, device stability, low lasing threshold and so on [72-76]. Therefore, whether gelation or not become one concise standard to select the solvent for optical ink formula in printed electronics. Superstructure identification of physical gels becomes one platform to understand the rheological process during the film-forming procedures.

PPFOH-Based Supramolecular Conjugated Polymers

We demonstrate supramolecular functionalization of polyfluorenes to design and synthesize several models of supramolecular conjugated polymers (SPS) such as polyfluorenols that here is called as PPFOH by the introduction of hydrogen bonds (Figure 4), and poly(diazafluorenes) with the C-H···N bond and the ability of coordination or protons, PODPF with pendent both Van der Waals bonding and steric bulky groups [77-79]. We first examine the assemble behaviors of PPFOH-based supramolecular conjugated polymers to tune aggregates and thin film morphology. PPFOH can assemble into physical gels in toluene with a critical gelation concentration (CGC) of 20 mg ml^{-1} at room temperature. This result suggest that PPFOH are easier than PFO to organize into supramolecular cross linking network than PFO after the introduction of strong intermolecular forces of hydrogen bonds. Supramolecular conjugated polymers are not only favorable for the formation of supramolecular gel networks, but also for the molecular assembly into nanostructures with various dimensionalities. As shown in Figure 4, PPFOH are also can assemble into hierarchically nano, micro, or macro and even millimeter-scale particles via reprecipitation at the different concentration of PPFOHs. Supramolecular conjugated polymer nanoparticles with the size ranging from 200 to 40 nm were obtained when adding H_2O in DMF solution [80]. Furthermore, the sizes of nanoparticles are decreased with the increase of the addition of the amounts of H_2O. In addition, this particle are probably supramolecular conjugated polymer nanogels if you consider the above the gelation and data of dynamic light scattering, although the robust characterization still require to provide.

Supramolecular Electroluminescence

PPFOH exhibit not only abundant assembled structures, but also the unique aggregate luminescence behaviors. We found the big molecular weight and solvent effect of PPFOH-based SCPs on the photophysics. The effects of gelation and nongelation solution on emission have been examine. PPFOH have two peaks of ~420 and ~440 nm that are similar with single chain polyfluorene in dilute nongelation solvents such as THF, while one red-shift peak at ~430 nm was only observed in dilute gelation solvents such as chloroform and toluene ($c = 0.01$ mg/ml). These result indicated that PPFOH have two basic structures, including the interchain complex (I) and chain-solvent complex (II), as shown in Figure 4. One important observation is green emission of PPFOH at 530-550 nm that is similar to the controversial g-band in PLEDs that was observed early by Pei et al. in 1996 [81]. Hypothesis on the origin of g-band are always disputed, either the aggregates (excimers) or ketone defects. The frontier is physical process, the latter is chemical process, associated with the oxidation. Despite the most research agree on the ketone defect, our observation supported the aggregate mechanism. Aggregate emission of PPFOH can be observed in thin films spin coated from both gelation and nongelation solution, as shown in Figure 4. The difference is their intensity of g-band, the stronger in nongelation solution such as THF than that in toluene. Aggregate emission have the essence of supramolecular luminescence that can be supported by the g-band emission in concentrated THF solution, in which oxidation and thermal decomposition were excluded easily. Furthermore, g-band in oligofluorenol (TFOH) have been prove to be reversible by titration experiments. The hydrogen bonds have been monitored by concentration-dependent nuclear magnetic resonance (NMR) [82]. These results suggest PPFOH can generate the supramolecular complex aggregates that consists of the multiple polymer chains. The intensity of g-band in thin films spin coated from gelation solvents such as toluene is weaker than that from nongelation solvents such as THF, indicated supramolecular precursor structures should be considered in the process of ink formula for the printing electronic devices. The supramolecular luminescence also suggested that aggregate bulk homojunction structures exist in PPFOH thin films that will be waited for the confirmation of AFM and other tools. Finally, PPFOH can be tunable RGB and multiple colors such as blue, green and yellow as well as other by the variation of molecular weight and solvents, even other additives. PPFOH-based SCPN have different from PFO without emission change. Size-controllable PPFOH nanoparticles exhibit size-dependent luminescence behaviors that are similar to the phenomena in inorganic quantum dots. Intensity of g-band emission become stronger when the size of nanoparticle become smaller, which probably contributed to the FRET from in-situ aggregate structures to the isotropic chains of polyfluorenol. PPFOH nanoparticle with the sizes of ~80 nm exhibit nearly white light emission spectra with the CIE coordinates (0.30, 0.42). As a result, PLEDs with the configuration of Au/p-SiC/PPFOH nanoparticles/ITO have been fabricated with supramolecular white emission color with CIE (0.31, 0.34) at 20 V. Supramolecular electroluminescence spectra can be fitted by three Gaussian profiles at around 433, 474, and 535 nm. To this end, the investigation of supramolecular conjugated polymers makes us set up the supramolecular electroluminescence. Supramolecular luminescence and EL have been achieved by PPFOH that can differ from molecular luminescence by comparison with dilute solution to concentrated solution or thin films. Molecular luminescence is the emission bands that can be observed in the very dilute solution that can be regarded as single molecular state. In sharp contrast, supramolecular luminescence is the aggregate emissions in concentrated solutions, thin films as well as devices. Despite supramolecular luminescence has some drawbacks such as low efficiency, they have several advantages over molecular luminescence. Supramolecular luminescence is very sensitive to environment. This character offer versatile platform to thin film luminescent sensors. Supramolecular electroluminescence in organic semiconductors will be merits such as stimulus-responsive feature, self-healing feature, soft mechanical features and others over conventional conjugate polymers, which also expended the application of organic thin film sensors and actuators due to the above mentioned excellent quality. Supramolecular conjugated polymers will be coined as soft semiconductors that push toward era of consciousness with a label of artificial intelligence robotics in organic mechatronics.

CONCLUSION

The universe four-element philosophy of matter-energy-information-consciousness (MEIC) can be transformed into the chemical four-element theory of polymer semiconductors that are electronic structure, steric hindrance, conformation and topology, as well as supramolecular force [83]. Among them, supramolecular behaviors dominate functional complexity and high-ordered motions in organic systemic devices. Herein, we explore supramolecular approach to plastic electronics, focusing on the PLEDs and polymer nonvolatile memory devices. The state-of-the-art concept of supramolecular polymer semiconductors (SPS) have been proposed to integrate the optoelectronic and supramolecular feature into one polymer with the multifunction. As a result, four unique individual features of SPSs in solution or thin films have been demonstrated, including reversible conformational transition, molecular tweezer effect, molecular assembly, and aggregate luminescence in the state-of-the-art models of PVK-based π-stacked polymer semiconductors and polyfluorenol-based supramolecular π-conjugated polymers. These features have been applied to organic devices, resulting in the important progress in plastic electronics. Tweezer conformation of PVK enable suppressing the emission or aggregates to achieve the deep-blue electroluminescence of pyrene-based fluorescent materials in PLED. Hindrance-functionalized stacked polymers are favorable for the reversible switching between partially eclipsed isomers and face-to-face stacking conformation under the electrical field, achieving the rewritable/erasable polymer nonvolatile flash memories with the mechanism of phase change. Nonvolitalile flash memory device exhibit the turn-on of 2.5, on/off ratio is about 10^4, and retention time of 10^8. PPFOH exhibit excellent assembled ability under the drive force of stacking interaction and hydrogen bonding to form the physical gels with supramolecular cross-linking networks, nanoparticles and nanogels, as well as bulk homojunction thin films. Secondary non-covalent forces drive the conformation entanglement and aggregates, in turn resulting in the essence of color-tunable supramolecular electroluminescence with extreme big effect of solvents and molecular weight. White PLED have been achieved by supramolecular electroluminescence of PPFOH-based nanoparticles. To this end, we set up the supramolecular resistive switching of π-stacked polymer semiconductors and supramolecular electroluminescence of supramolecular conjugated polymers.

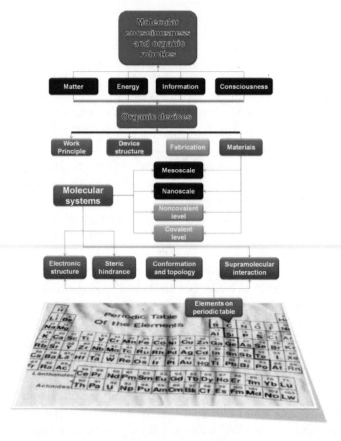

Figure 5. A schematic big chemical blueprint on periodic table of the elements (blueprint-on-table) that have been drawn by CMSOD.

Outlook

When flexible, stretchable, weavable and wearable electrodes were adopted in organic thin film or fiber devices, a trend that surface equals device will spread extensively in the whole world of human being. Organic devices become the interface between molecular world and human being' world. Organic devices will make everything smarts and change our daily life dramatically in post-information age. On that basis, SPSs with the excellent stimuli-responsive feature to various photo, electronic, magnetic, mechano, thermal, sonic signals will update organic electronics into supramolecular mechatronics. Organic multiple-input multiple-output (MIMO) stimuli-responsive devices probably create machine consciousness by activating molecular information toward the era of consciousness. In order to guide us explore functonal molecular systems and organic devices, we proposed a three-dimensional periodic table of the elements to link atoms and devices as well as their systems as shown in Figure 5. The big blueprint on periodic table of the elements (blueprint-on-table) require hierarchical chemistry that should be introduced to active molecular functionalities in organic devices via nanoscale and meso-scale synergetic operation beyond four-element molecular design [84-85]. Ultimately, scientist will master physical laws that drive the motion of molecular nanoobjects that in turn drive the motion of the macro-worlds. Smart organic devices will become one solution to artificial intelligence robotics. We prospect that a new era of consciousness are coming when personal robotics walk into home according to the self-similar four-element theory that were extracted from universe, nature, life and social society.

ACKNOWLEDGMENTS

We express our sincere gratitude to the National Natural Science Funds for Excellent Young Scholar (21322402), National Natural Science Foundation of China (U1301243, 21274064, 21144004, 60876010, 61177029, 20974046), The Program for New Century Excellent Talents in University (NCET-11-0992), Doctoral Fund of Ministry of Education of China (20133223110007), Excellent science and technology innovation team of Jiangsu Higher Education Institutions (2013), Natural Science Foundation of Jiangsu Province, China (BK2011761, BK2008053, SJ209003, BM2012010).

Project funded by the Priority Academic Program Development of Jiangsu Higher Education Institutions, PAPD (YX03001).

REFERENCES

[1] Forrest, S. R. *Nature.* 2004, *428*, 911-918.

[2] Xie, L.-H.; Yin, C.-R.; Lai, W.-Y.; Fan, Q.-L.; Huang, W. *Prog. Polym. Sci..* 2012, *37*, 1192-1264.

[3] Friend, R. H.; Gymer, R. W.; Holmes, A. B.; Burroughes, J. H.; Marks, R. N.; Taliani, C.; Bradley, D. D. C.; Dos Santos, D. A.; Bredas, J. L.; Logdlund, M.; Salaneck, W. R. *Nature.* 1999, *397*, 121-128.

[4] Tang, C. W.; Vanslyke, S. A. *Appl. Phys. Lett..* 1987, *51*, 913-915.

[5] Chiang, C. K.; Fincher, C. R.; Park, Y. W.; Heeger, A. J.; Shirakawa, H.; Louis, E. J.; Gau, S. C.; MacDiarmid, A. G. *Phys.Rev. Lett..* 1977, *39*, 1098-1101.

[6] Burroughes, J. H.; Bradley, D. D. C.; Brown, A. R.; Marks, R. N.; Mackay, K.; Friend, R. H.; Burns, P. L.; Holmes, A. B. *Nature.* 1990, *347*, 539-541.

[7] Bao, Z.; Dodabalapur, A.; Lovinger, A. J. *Appl. Phys. Lett..* 1996, *69*, 4108-4110.

[8] Guenes, S.; Neugebauer, H.; Sariciftci, N. S. *Chem. Rev..* 2007, *107*, 1324-1338.

[9] Liu, J.; Yin, Z.; Cao, X.; Zhao, F.; Lin, A.; Xie, L.; Fan, Q.; Boey, F.; Zhang, H.; Huang, W. *Acs Nano.* 2010, *4*, 3987-3992.

[10] Samuel, I. D. W.; Turnbull, G. A. *Chem. Rev..* 2007, *107*, 1272-1295.

[11] Xie, L,-H.; Huang, W. 14th Optoelectronics and Communications Conference (OECC); IEEE: HK, 2009; Vol. 2013, pp 492-493.

[12] Stupp, S. I.; LeBonheur, V.; Walker, K.; Li, L. S.; Huggins, K. E.; Keser, M.; Amstutz, A. *Science.* 1997, *276*, 384-389.

[13] Hawker, C. J.; Hedrick, J. L.; Miller, R. D.; Volksen, W. *Mrs Bull..* 2000, *25*, 54-58.

[14] Meijer, E. W.; Schenning, A. *Nature.* 2002, *419*, 353-354.

[15] Hoeben, F. J. M.; Jonkheijm, P.; Meijer, E. W.; Schenning, A. *Chem. Rev..* 2005, *105*, 1491-1546.

[16] Schenning, A.; Meijer, E. W. *Chem. Commun..* 2005, 3245-3258.

[17] Grozema, F. C.; Siebbeles, L. D. A. *Int. Rev. Phys. Chem..* 2008, *27*, 87-138.

[18] Yamamoto, Y.; Fukushima, T.; Suna, Y.; Ishii, N.; Saeki, A.; Seki, S.;

Tagawa, S.; Taniguchi, M.; Kawai, T.; Aida, T. *Science.* 2006, *314*, 1761-1764.

[19] Hill, J. P.; Jin, W. S.; Kosaka, A.; Fukushima, T.; Ichihara, H.; Shimomura, T.; Ito, K.; Hashizume, T.; Ishii, N.; Aida, T. *Science.* 2004, *304*, 1481-1483.

[20] Wurthner, F.; Chen, Z. J.; Hoeben, F. J. M.; Osswald, P.; You, C. C.; Jonkheijm, P.; von Herrikhuyzen, J.; Schenning, A.; van der Schoot, P.; Meijer, E. W.; Beckers, E. H. A.; Meskers, S. C. J.; Janssen, R. A. J. *J. Am. Chem. Soc..* 2004, *126*, 10611-10618.

[21] Sakai, N.; Bhosale, R.; Emery, D.; Mareda, J.; Matile, S. *J. Am. Chem. Soc..* 2010, *132*, 6923-6925.

[22] Bhosale, R.; Misek, J.; Sakai, N.; Matile, S. *Chem. Soc. Rev..* 2010, *39*, 138-149.

[23] Bhosale, R.; Perez-Velasco, A.; Ravikumar, V.; Kishore, R. S. K.; Kel, O.; Gomez-Casado, A.; Jonkheijm, P.; Huskens, J.; Maroni, P.; Borkovec, M.; Sawada, T.; Vauthey, E.; Sakai, N.; Matile, S. *Angew. Chem. Int. Ed..* 2009, *48*, 6461-6464.

[24] Faramarzi, V.; Niess, F.; Moulin, E.; Maaloum, M.; Dayen, J.-F.; Beaufrand, J.-B.; Zanettini, S.; Doudin, B.; Giuseppone, N. *Nature Chem..* 2012, *4*, 485-490.

[25] Giuseppone, N. *Acc. Chem. Res..* 2012, *45*, 2178-2188.

[26] Moulin, E.; Niess, F.; Maaloum, M.; Buhler, E.; Nyrkova, I.; Giuseppone, N. *Angew. Chem. Int. Ed..* 2010, *49*, 6974-6978.

[27] Busseron, E.; Ruff, Y.; Moulin, E.; Giuseppone, N. *Nanoscale.* 2013, *5*, 7098-7140.

[28] Abbel, R.; Grenier, C.; Pouderoijen, M. J.; Stouwdam, J. W.; Leclere, P. E. L. G.; Sijbesma, R. P.; Meijer, E. W.; Schenning, A. P. H. J. *J. Am. Chem. Soc..* 2009, *131*, 833-843.

[29] Korevaar, P. A.; George, S. J.; Markvoort, A. J.; Smulders, M. M. J.; Hilbers, P. A. J.; Schenning, A. P. H. J.; De Greef, T. F. A.; Meijer, E. W. *Nature.* 2012, *481*, 492-U103.

[30] Korevaar, P. A.; de Greef, T. F. A.; Meijer, E. W. *Chem. Mater..* 2014, *26*, 576-586.

[31] Babu, S. S.; Praveen, V. K.; Ajayaghosh, A. *Chem. Rev..* 2014, *114*, 1973-2129.

[32] Ajayaghosh, A.; George, S. J. *J. Am. Chem. Soc..* 2001, *123*, 5148-5149.

[33] Glowacki, E. D.; Irimia-Vladu, M.; Kaltenbrunner, M.; Gasiorowski, J.; White, M. S.; Monkowius, U.; Romanazzi, G.; Suranna, G. P.; Mastrorilli, P.; Sekitani, T.; Bauer, S.; Someya, T.; Torsi, L.; Sariciftci,

N. S. *Adv. Mater.*. 2013, *25*, 1563-1569.

[34] Aida, T.; Meijer, E. W.; Stupp, S. I. *Science.* 2012, *335*, 813-817.

[35] Fernandez, G.; Perez, E. M.; Sanchez, L.; Martin, N. *Angew. Chem. Int. Ed.*. 2008, *47*, 1094-1097.

[36] Emilio M. Pérez; Nazario Martín, Solar & Alternative Energy; SPIE: San Diego, 2009. (DOI: 10.1117/2.1200905.1657)

[37] Xie, L.-H.; Chang, Y.-Z.; Gu, J.-F.; Sun, R.-J.; Li, J.-W.; Zhao, X.-H.; Huang, W. *Acta Phys. Chim. Sin.*. 2010, *26*, 1784-1794.

[38] Ren, B.-Y.; Ou, C.-J.; Zhang, C.; Chang, Y.-Z.; Yi, M.-D.; Liu, J.-Q.; Xie, L.-H.; Zhang, G.-W.; Deng, X.-Y.; Li, S.-B.; Wei, W.; Huang, W. *J. Phys. Chem. C.* 2012, *116*, 8881-8887.

[39] Schroder, D.; Loos, J.; Schwarz, H.; Thissen, R.; Dutuit, O. *J. Phys. Chem. A.* 2004, *108*, 9931-9937.

[40] Evans, R. C. *J. Mater. Chem. C.* 2013, *1*, 4190-4200.

[41] Cacialli, F.; Wilson, J. S.; Michels, J. J.; Daniel, C.; Silva, C.; Friend, R. H.; Severin, N.; Samori, P.; Rabe, J. P.; O'Connell, M. J.; Taylor, P. N.; Anderson, H. L. *Nat. Mater.*. 2002, *1*, 160-164.

[42] Kim, B.-G.; Jeong, E. J.; Chung, J. W.; Seo, S.; Koo, B.; Kim, J. *Nat. Mater.*. 2013, *12*, 659-664.

[43] Facchetti, A. *Nat. Mater.*. 2013, *12*, 598-600.

[44] Wang, C.; Dong, H.; Hu, W.; Liu, Y.; Zhu, D. *Chem. Rev.*. 2012, *112*, 2208-2267.

[45] Yang, Y.; Zhao, J.-F.; Liu, R.-R.; Li, J.-W.; Yi, M.-D.; Xie, G.-H.; Xie, L.-H.; Chang, Y.-Z.; Yin, C.-R.; Zhou, X.-H.; Zhao, Y.; Qian, Y.; Huang, W. *Tetrahedron.* 2013, *69*, 6317-6322.

[46] Hu, C.-P.; Liu, Y.-Y.; Xie, L.-H.; Li, J.-W.; Li, Y.-R.; Tai, Q.; Yi, M.-D.; Huang, W. *Chem. Phys. Lett.*. 2013, *578*, 150-155.

[47] Li, J.; Liu, Y.; Qian, Y.; Li, L.; Xie, L.; Shang, J.; Yu, T.; Yi, M.; Huang, W. *PCCP.* 2013, *15*, 12694-12701.

[48] Scheuring, S.; Sturgis, J. N.; Prima, V.; Bernadac, A.; Levy, D.; Rigaud, J. L. *PNAS.* 2004, *101*, 11293-11297.

[49] Beljonne, D.; Curutchet, C.; Scholes, G. D.; Silbey, R. J. *J. Phys. Chem. B.* 2009, *113*, 6583-6599.

[50] Doust, A. B.; Wilk, K. E.; Curmi, P. M. G.; Scholes, G. D. *J. Photochem. Photobiol. A Chem.*. 2006, *184*, 1-17.

[51] Genereux, J. C.; Wuerth, S. M.; Barton, J. K. *J. Am. Chem. Soc.*. 2011, *133*, 3863-3868.

[52] Genereux, J. C.; Barton, J. K. *Chem. Rev.*. 2010, *110*, 1642-1662.

[53] Grozema, F. C.; Tonzani, S.; Berlin, Y. A.; Schatz, G. C.; Siebbeles, L.

D. A.; Ratner, M. A. *J. Am. Chem. Soc.*. 2009, *131*, 14204-14205.

[54] Guo, X.; Gorodetsky, A. A.; Hone, J.; Barton, J. K.; Nuckolls, C. *Nat. Nanotechnol.*. 2008, *3*, 163-167.

[55] Porath, D.; Bezryadin, A.; de Vries, S.; Dekker, C. *Nature.* 2000, *403*, 635-638.

[56] Xie, L.-H.; Ling, Q.-D.; Hou, X.-Y.; Huang, W. *J. Am. Chem. Soc.*. 2008, *130*, 2120-2121.

[57] Peason, J. M.; Stolka, M. Poly(N-Vinylcarbazole); Gordon & Breach: New York, 1981.

[58] Hari Singh Nalwa, Advanced Functional Molecules and Polymers; Gordon & Breach: New York, 2001; Vol. 3.

[59] Liu, F.; Tang, C.; Chen, Q.-Q.; Shi, F.-F.; Wu, H.-B.; Xie, L.-H.; Peng, B.; Wei, W.; Cao, Y.; Huang, W. *J. Phys. Chem. C.* 2009, *113*, 4641-4647.

[60] Liu, F.; Xie, L.-H.; Tang, C.; Liang, J.; Chen, Q.-Q.; Peng, B.; Wei, W.; Cao, Y.; Huang, W. *Org. Lett.*. 2009, *11*, 3850-3853.

[61] Yin, C.-R.; Ye, S.-H.; Zhao, J.; Yi, M.-D.; Xie, L.-H.; Lin, Z.-Q.; Chang, Y.-Z.; Liu, F.; Xu, H.; Shi, N.-E.; Qian, Y.; Huang, W. *Macromolecules.* 2011, *44*, 4589-4595.

[62] Xie, L.-H.; Deng, X.-Y.; Chen, L.; Chen, S.-F.; Liu, R.-R.; Hou, X.-Y.; Wong, K.-Y.; Ling, Q.-D.; Huang, W. *J. Polym. Sci., Part A: Polym. Chem.*. 2009, *47*, 5221-5229.

[63] H.-E. Schaefer, Nanoscience; Springer: Berlin Heidelberg, 2010. (DOI 10.1007/978-3-642-10559-3_9)

[64] Xie, L.-H.; Hou, X.-Y.; Hua, Y.-R.; Huang, Y.-Q.; Zhao, B.-M.; Liu, F.; Peng, B.; Wei, W.; Huang, W. *Org. Lett.*. 2007, *9*, 1619-1622.

[65] Yin, C.-R.; Han, Y.; Li, L.; Ye, S.-H.; Mao, W.-W.; Yi, M.-D.; Ling, H.-F.; Xie, L.-H.; Zhang, G.-W.; Huang, W. *Polym. Chem.*. 2013, *4*, 2540-2545.

[66] Bandyopadhyay, A.; Pal, A. J. *Appl. Phys. Lett.*. 2004, *84*, 999-1001.

[67] Cheah, C. L.; Ali, B. M.; Mahdi, M. A.; Abdullah, M. K. *Photonic Netw. Commun.*. 2006, *12*, 173-180.

[68] Lim, S. L.; Ling, Q.; Teo, E. Y. H.; Zhu, C. X.; Chan, D. S. H.; Kang, E.-T.; Neoh, K. G. *Chem. Mater.*. 2007, *19*, 5148-5157.

[69] Ye, S.-H.; Yin, C.-R.; Zhou, Z.; Hu, T.-Q.; Li, Y.-H.; Li, L.; Xie, L.-H.; Huang, W. *J. Polym. Sci., Part B: Polym. Phys.*. 2014, *52*, 587-595.

[70] Lin, Z.-Q.; Shi, N.-E.; Li, Y.-B.; Qiu, D.; Zhang, L.; Lin, J.-Y.; Zhao, J.-F.; Wang, C.; Xie, L.-H.; Huang, W. *J. Phys. Chem. C.* 2011, *115*, 4418-4424.

[71] Zhang, X.; Hu, Q.; Lin, J.; Lei, Z.; Guo, X.; Xie, L.; Lai, W.; Huang, W. *Appl. Phys. Lett..* 2013, *103*.

[72] Lu, H.-H.; Liu, C.-Y.; Chang, C.-H.; Chen, S.-A. *Adv. Mater..* 2007, *19*, 2574-2579.

[73] Prins, P.; Grozema, F. C.; Nehls, B. S.; Farrell, T.; Scherf, U.; Siebbeles, L. D. A. *Phys. Rev. B.* 2006, 74, 113203.

[74] Hung, M. C.; Liao, J. L.; Chen, S. A.; Chen, S. H.; Su, A. C. *J. Am. Chem. Soc..* 2005, *127*, 14576-14577.

[75] Ryu, G.; Stavrinou, P. N.; Bradley, D. D. C. *Adv. Funct. Mater..* 2009, *19*, 3237-3242.

[76] Rothe, C.; Galbrecht, F.; Scherf, U.; Monkman, A. *Adv. Mater..* 2006, *18*, 2137-2140.

[77] Lin, J.; Yu, Z.; Zhu, W.; Xing, G.; Lin, Z.; Yang, S.; Xie, L.; Niu, C.; Huang, W. *Polym. Chem..* 2013, *4*, 477-483.

[78] Li, W.-J.; Liu, B.; Qian, Y.; Xie, L.-H.; Wang, J.; Li, S.-B.; Huang, W. *Polym. Chem..* 2013, *4*, 1796-1802.

[79] Lin, J.-Y.; Zhu, W.-S.; Liu, F.; Xie, L.-H.; Zhang, L.; Xia, R.; Xing, G.-C.; Huang, W. *Macromolecules.* 2014, *47*, 1001-1007.

[80] Lin, J.-Y.; Wong J.-I.; Xie, L.-H.; Dong X.-C.; Yang H.-Y.; Huang, W. *Macro. Rap. Commun.* 2014, DOI: 10.1002/marc.201300831.

[81] Pei, Q. B.; Yang, Y. *J. Am. Chem. Soc..* 1996, *118*, 7416-7417.

[82] Zhang, G.-W.; Wang, L.; Xie, L.-H.; Lin, J.-Y.; Huang, W. *Int. J. Mol. Sci..* 2013, *14*, 22368-22379.

[83] Xie, L.-H; Huang, W, Advances in Science; Science Network: Canada, 2013; Vol. 1, Chapter 4, 104-127.

[84] Chang, Y.-Z.; Shao, Q.; Bai, L.-Y.; Ou, C.-J.; Lin, J.-Y.; Xie, L.-H.; Liu, Z.-D.; Chen, X.; Zhang, G.-W.; Huang, W. *Small.* 2013, *9*, 3218-3223.

[85] Zhang, G.-W.; Wang, L.; Xie, L.-H.; Hou, X.-Y.; Liu, Z.-D.; Huang, W. *J. Nanomater..* 2013, 2013, 8.

In: Advances in Optoelectronics Research   ISBN: 978-1-63321-211-4
Editor: Marcus R. Oswald   © 2014 Nova Science Publishers, Inc.

Chapter 3

ELASTICO-MECHANOLUMINESCENT MATERIALS: PREPARATION, PROPERTIES, MECHANISM AND APPLICATIONS

Jun-Cheng Zhang,[1,2,*] *Yun-Ze Long,*[1,2] *Xusheng Wang*[3]
and Chao-Nan Xu[4,5]

[1]College of Physics, Qingdao University, Qingdao, P.R. China
[2]Key Laboratory of Photonics Materials and Technology
in Universities of Shandong, Qingdao University, Qingdao, P.R. China
[3]Functional Materials Research Laboratory,
Tongji University, Shanghai, P.R. China
[4]National Institute of Advanced Industrial Science and Technology,
Saga, Japan
[5]International Institute for Carbon Neutral Energy Research
(WPI-I2CNER), Kyushu University, Fukuoka, Japan

ABSTRACT

Elastico-mechanoluminescence (EML) materials are a newly developed type of mechano-optical convertible inorganic phosphors. They can respond to different mechanical stress stimuli such as touch, impact, vibration, friction, stretching, compression, bend, and twist as light emission. More importantly, these materials possess an accurate

---

* Email:jc-zhang@qdu.edu.cn (J. C. Zhang).

linear dependence of EML intensity on the stress parameters (including intensity, energy and deformation rate) in the elastic limit. A stress sensitive coating prepared by the homogeneous dispersion of the EML indicators into an optical binder matrix can simultaneously "feel" (sense) and "see" (image) various mechanical stresses over a wide energy and frequency range. The EML intensity distribution directly reflects the stress distribution of the coating subjected to stresses. In view of the advantages of wireless, non-destructive, reproducible, real-time and reliable *in situ* stress sensing, EML materials have important application prospects as stress probe in the stress detecting field of life sciences, robot manufacturing, construction safety monitoring, aeronautics and astronautics. However, the research history on EML is relatively short, only about fifteen years since EML was first reported in 1999. There are still several urgent problems to be resolved before the wide practical applications of EML materials could be realized. In this chapter, the EML materials and EML development history are briefly introduced. Subsequently, the preparation method of EML materials and coating, the EML properties, mechanism, and applications are summarized. Finally, the challenges and perspectives of EML materials are discussed.

1. INTRODUCTION

Mechanoluminescence (ML) is a type of luminescence induced by the application of mechanical energy to solid materials [1]. ML can be excited by any stress action, including compressing, stretching, bending, loading, shaking, cutting, cleaving, grinding, scratching, crushing or impulsive deformation. The phenomenon of ML has been known for more than four centuries since it was reported by Francis Bacon in 1605, who observed sparkling light when breaking sugar crystals. Roughly 50% of all organic and inorganic solids exhibit ML behavior, such as quartz, sugar, alkali halide, II–VI compounds, metals, phosphors, minerals, silica glass, piezoelectric complex, and polymer crystals [2,3]. Generally ML can be divided into elastico-ML (EML), plastico-ML (PML), and fracto-ML (FML); they correspond to the light emission induced by elastic deformation, plastic deformation, and fracture of solids, respectively [4]. It should be noted that, contrary to destructive FML, EML and PML belong to nondestructive ML, which is very promising for the practical application from the viewpoint of reproducibility.

Compared to PML and FML materials, only a few solid materials show EML during their elastic deformation. Since the EML properties of

$SrAl_2O_4:Eu^{2+}$ (green) [5] and $ZnS:Mn^{2+}$ (yellow) [6] were first reported in 1999, researchers have devoted their careers to searching and investigating EML materials. To date more than twenty kinds of inorganic piezoelectric materials exhibiting excellent EML performance have been successfully developed.

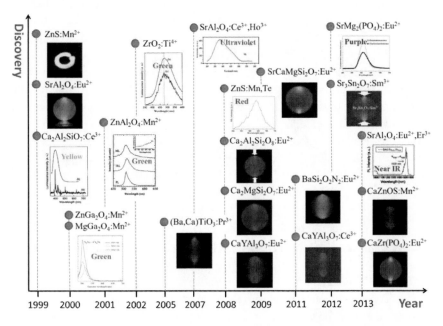

Figure 1. Development history of elastico-mechanoluminescece (EML) materials [5-24].

Figure 1 shows the development history of EML materials. These materials are mainly common silicate, aluminate, titanate and phosphate systems, and other gallate, oxide, nitroxide and stannate, including $ZnGa_2O_4:Mn^{2+}$ (green) [7], $MgGa_2O_4:Mn^{2+}$ (green) [7], $ZnAl_2O_4:Mn^{2+}$ (green) [8], $ZrO_2:Ti^{4+}$ (green) [9], $Ca_2Al_2SiO_7:Ce^{3+}$ (yellow) [10], $(Ba,Ca)TiO_3:Pr^{3+}$ (red) [11], $SrAl_2O_4:Ce^{3+},Ho^{3+}$ (ultraviolet) [12], $Ca_2Al_2Si_2O_8:Eu^{2+}$ (blue) [13], $Ca_2MgSi_2O_7:Eu^{2+}$ (green) [14], $CaYAl_3O_7:Eu^{2+}$ (blue) [15], ZnS: Mn, Te (red) [16], $SrCaMgSi_2O_7:Eu^{2+}$ (bluish-green) [17], $BaSi_2O_2N_2:Eu^{2+}$ (bluish-green) [18,19], $CaYAl_3O_7:Ce^{3+}$ (deep blue) [20], $SrMg_2(PO_4)_2:Eu^{2+}$ (purple) [21], $Sr_3Sn_2O_7:Sm^{3+}$ (reddish-orange) [22], $SrAl_2O_4:Eu^{2+},Er^{3+}$ (infrared) [23], $CaZnOS:Mn^{2+}$ (red) [24], and $CaZr(PO_4)_2:Eu^{2+}$ (cyan) [25]. As indicated in above curved brackets, the available colors of EML cover a broad spectral range from ultraviolet light to infrared light, which has different usages. More important, these materials possess an accurate linear dependence of EML intensity on the various stress parameters, such as intensity, energy and deformation rate, in the elastic limit. A stress sensitive coating prepared by the homogeneous dispersion of the EML indicators into an optical binder matrix can simultaneously "feel" (sense) and "see" (image) various mechanical stresses over a wide energy and frequency range. The EML intensity distribution directly reflects the stress distribution of the coating subjected to stresses. In view of the advantages of wireless, non-destructive, reproducible, real-time and reliable *in situ* stress sensing, EML materials have important application prospects as stress probe in the stress detecting field of life sciences, robot manufacturing, construction safety monitoring, aeronautics and astronautics.

In this chapter, based on our recent research results, the preparation method of EML materials and coating, the EML properties, mechanism, and applications are briefly introduced. The challenges and perspectives of EML materials are also discussed.

2. MATERIAL SYNTHESIS AND COATING PREPARATION

The EML materials are normally synthesized by high temperature solid-phase reaction, which is the simplest operation. Take CaZnOS:Mn^{2+} for example, the raw materials of $CaCO_3$, ZnS and $MnCO_3$ were thoroughly ground according to the stoichiometric amounts, pressed into pellets, and subsequently sintered at 1100 °C for 3 h in an argon atmosphere. The polycrystalline product of CaZnOS:Mn^{2+} was ground and screened through a 20 μm sieve. As a result, EML coating can be applied in uniform layers on the surface of the target objects by mixing the EML particles with optical binders and polymers. Different coating techniques such as spin coating and spray coating can be selected according to the practical condition. The thickness of the resultant coating can also be controlled from micrometer to millimeter.

Figure 2 shows a multiple stress-sensitive coating prepared by the homogeneous dispersion of EML indicators into an optical elastic matrix. The EML particles in this coating are like a neuron which responds to external stimuli, while the elastic matrix serves as a packaging material to retain the network of neurons, and transmits external mechanical contacts to the EML particles. When the stress-sensitive coating is subjected to various mechanical stresses, such as ultrasonic vibration, impact, friction, compression, and so on, the local contact stress is converted into a measurable luminescence signal by the EML particles, thus the EML image and the luminescence signal can be recorded by both the digital camera and photomultiplier tube (PMT) detector. The recorded EML intensities are modulated on the application of various mechanical stresses to the stress-sensitive coating, which results in a stress distribution image. This EML coating, just like skin, could be distributed over a model surface with an arbitrary shape. Its nondestructive and non-invasive characteristics indicate promising potential as touch sensors or smart skin in a complex structure.

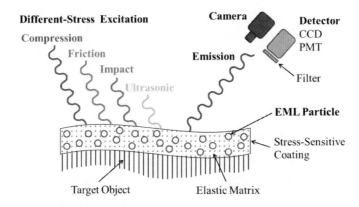

Figure 2. Schematic representation of stress-sensitive coating.

3. ELASTICO-MECHANOLUMINESCENT PROPERTIES

For the practical applications in the detection and monitoring of various stress stimulus, the EML materials are required to have several necessary characteristics as following: prompt response, intense EML, multi-stress sensitivity, linear relation between EML and stress parameter, wide measurement range for the dynamic load, repeatability, water resistance, and so on.

3.1. Multi-Stress Sensitivity

All the developed EML materials give the prompt luminescence response under the stress stimulus with enough intensity. The response time is no more than millisecond scale. A few EML materials, such as $SrAl_2O_4:Eu^{2+}$, $ZnS:Mn^{2+}$, $(Ba,Ca)TiO_3:Pr^{3+}$, $BaSi_2O_2N_2:Eu^{2+}$, $Sr_3Sn_2O_7:Sm^{3+}$, $CaZnOS:Mn^{2+}$, and $CaZr(PO_4)_2:Eu^{2+}$, have been found to possess intense EML. However, among them, the categories of EML materials which could response to different stresses are relatively less, including $SrAl_2O_4:Eu^{2+}$ [3], $ZnS:Mn^{2+}$ [3], $BaSi_2O_2N_2:Eu^{2+}$ [19], and $CaZnOS:Mn^{2+}$ [24].

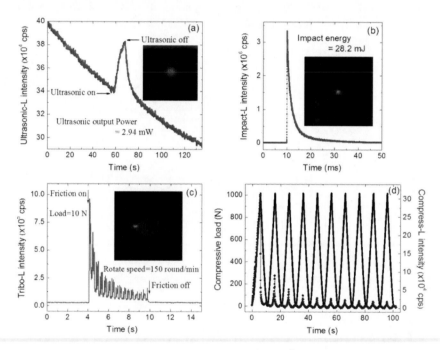

Figure 3. Multi-stress sensitive behaviors of $CaZnOS:Mn^{2+}$. (a) Ultrasonic-L response, (b) Impact-L response, (c) Tribo-L response, and (d) Compress-L response. Insets are the EML pictures.

Figure 3 presents the ultrasonic vibration excited luminescence (Ultrasonic-L), impact excited luminescence (Impact-L), friction-excited luminescence (Tribo-L), and compression excited luminescence (Compress-L) of multi-stress sensitive $CaZnOS:Mn^{2+}$ [24].

Figure 3(a) shows the Ultrasonic-L excited by an applied ultrasonic fountain used for medical applications at a frequency of 20 MHz with an output power of 2.94 mW. An apparent luminescence signal was immediately measured when medical ultrasonic vibration was applied on the EML coating.

The Ultrasonic-L intensity increased sharply with increasing time of applied ultrasonic vibration.

When the ultrasonic power was turned off the EML luminescence was rapidly attenuated. The Ultrasonic-L image could be directly recorded by an intensified CCD gray scale camera [inset of Figure 3(a)]. It should be noted that a more intense Ultrasonic-L is obtained when ultrasonic vibrations of greater power (40 kHz, 4 W/cm^2) are applied to the film, levels usually used in glass and ceramic vessel cleaning. These results indicate that this EML material may sense ultrasonic vibration with a higher power and wider frequency range.

Figure 3(b) illustrates the strong Impact-L pulse. When a ball freely drops onto the EML coating, the Impact-L intensity sharply increases until it attains a peak value. The fitting calculation indicates that the decay time of Impact-L is less than 2.3 ms after the collision. The inset in Figure 3(b) shows the corresponding Impact-L image, in which an intense red gleam is observed.

This coating can also respond to friction (shear stress). A strong red Tribo-L is emitted in the contact position [inset of Figure 3(c)]. Figure 3(c) shows the Tribo-L intensity response. When friction is applied the Tribo-L intensity increases steeply and attains a peak value, then a periodic oscillation is observed, after which the luminescence intensity gradually decreases as the friction is maintained. The Tribo-L response immediately disappears when the friction force is turned off. The oscillation of Tribo-L has been shown to originate from inadequacies in the machine alignment and the non-uniformity of the sample setting [26]. Figure 3(d) shows the Compress-L behavior during reapplication of a compressive stress (10 consecutive cycles) at a constant deformation rate of 3 mm/min. In the first cycle the Compress-L intensity increased linearly with increasing compressive load, reaching an unsaturated peak value at the peak load (1000 N), followed by sharp attenuation on releasing the compressive load. In the later cycles the Compress-L peak intensity decayed significantly with stressed times. However, in each cycle the Compress-L intensity always changed linearly with the applied compressive load and showed a Compress-L peak at the load peak. Since the relation between Compress-L intensity and compressive load is linear, the EML brightness distribution [inset of Figure 1, CaZnOS:Mn^{2+}] reflects the stress distribution, which has been confirmed by previous simulation results [3,5,27].

3.2. Linear Relation

The linear relation between EML intensity and stress parameters has been found to be an intrinsic characteristic. In addition to the linear relation between EML intensity and compressive load, the linear relations between EML intensity and other stress parameters, including intensity, energy, and deformation rate, have been confirmed in $CaZnOS:Mn^{2+}$. Figures 4(a)-(b) present the accurate linear relation between Ultrasonic-L intensity and ultrasonic output power, Impact-L intensity with impact energy, Tribo-L intensity and load, and Compress-L intensity and deformation rate, respectively [24]. These quantitative relations imply that the $CaZnOS:Mn^{2+}$ EML film can sense various stresses and at the same time evaluate the corresponding stress parameters.

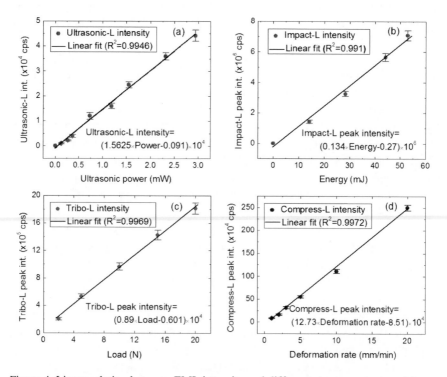

Figure 4. Linear relation between EML intensity and different stress parameters. (a) Ultrasonic-L intensity *vs.* ultrasonic output power, (b) Impact-L intensity *vs.* impact energy, (c) Tribo-L intensity *vs.* load, (d) Compress-L intensity *vs.* deformation rate.

3.3. Repeatability

The EML intensity of all the EML material decays with the repeating stressed times, such as the conditions shown in Figures 3(c) and (d). Importantly, the EML intensity will recover completely after the EML materials experienced the stress stimulus are irradiated with UV light (254 nm or 365 nm) for several minutes (normally 1 min). The same intense visible light emission could be observed again. It is obviously observed that the damage on the samples is very small after repetitive mechanical experiments, which is useful for repetitive application. Figure 5 shows the EML decay behaviors of $CaZnOS:Mn^{2+}$ and $(Ba,Ca)TiO_3:Pr^{3+}$ [28] and EML recovery effect of UV light irradiation. It is a phenomenon typically observed in EML materials of the so-called defect-controlled type, indicating the existence of charge traps which could be filled by the UV light irradiation. The decrease of EML intensity under the reapplication of various stresses is attributed the de-trapping process of the trapped carriers.

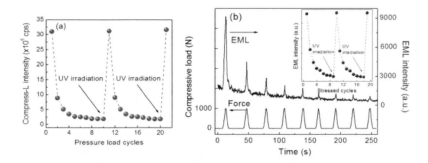

Figure 5. (a) EML decay and recovery behaviors of $CaZnOS:Mn^{2+}$. (b) Compress-L behavior of $(Ba,Ca)TiO_3:Pr^{3+}$ under the repeating compressive load. The inset shows its decay and recovery behaviors.

3.4. Water Resistance

It is well known that water resistance is one of the most importance properties for luminescent materials to realize the outdoor application, especially in moist or waterish environment. $SrAl_2O_4:Eu^{2+}$ had been considered to be the most promising EML materials because of intense brightness and high sensitivity even for weak stress, such as scratching or pressing with a fingernail. However, its EML disappears rapidly when it is immersed in water, due to hydrolysis, which limits the application. Therefore, EML materials exhibiting superior water resistance have been developed, such as $Ca_2Al_2SiO_7:Ce^{3+}$ [10], $CaAl_2Si_2O_8:Eu^{2+}$ [13], $Ca_2MgSi_2O_7:Eu^{2+},Dy^{3+}$ [14], $(Ba,Ca)TiO_3:Pr^{3+}$ [29], and $BaSi_2O_2N_2:Eu^{2+}$ [18].

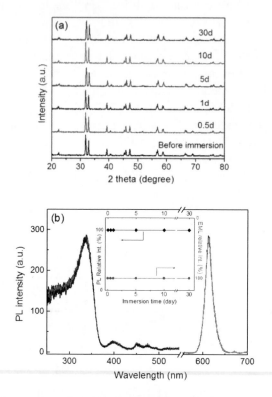

Figure 6. (a) XRD patterns and (b) photoluminescence (PL) spectra of $(Ba,Ca)TiO_3:Pr^{3+}$ with various immersion time. The inset of Figure 6(a) is the dependence of relative PL and EML intensities on immersion time.

Figure 6(a) shows the XRD patterns of $(Ba, Ca)TiO_3:Pr^{3+}$ with different water immersion time. There is no change in the peak positions and intensities even after 30 days immersion, indicating that the crystalline structure remains the same after water treatment. Their PL spectra are shown in Figure 6(b). The inset presents the immersion time dependence of the relative PL and ML intensities. All the samples maintain the same PL and EML intensities as those before immersion. The results clearly indicate the superior water resistance property of $(Ba, Ca)TiO_3:Pr^{3+}$.

4. ELASTICO-MECHANOLUMINESCENT MECHANISM

The previous reports indicated that the EML materials belong to piezoelectrically defect-controlled type of luminescent materials. The piezoelectric crystal structure and carrier traps with appropriate depth are the necessary characteristics for the EML materials. At present, there are mainly two models to explain EML mechanisms.

4.1. Piezoelectrically Induced Electroluminescence Model

Most of EML materials possess electroluminescence (EL) and EML functions at the same time, such as $SrAl_2O_4:Eu^{2+}$ [30], $ZnS:Mn^{2+}$ [6], $ZnAl_2O_4:Mn^{2+}$ [31], $(Ba, Ca)TiO_3:Pr^{3+}$ [11,32], $CaYAl_3O_7:Ce^{3+}$ [20], and $SrMg_2(PO_4)_2:Eu^{2+}$ [21]. This interesting multifunctional phenomenon provides a clue to understand the nature of EML mechanism. According to the relation between EL and EML, researchers have proposed a piezoelectrically induced electroluminescence (EL) model. When the stress is applied, a large piezoelectric field induced by the piezoelectric effect makes the trapped carriers de-trap and obtain enough energy to impact and excite luminescent centers to emit light. Diphase EML material $(Ba, Ca)TiO_3:Pr^{3+}$ is taken for the sample to discuss this EML mechanism in this section [28,29.32].

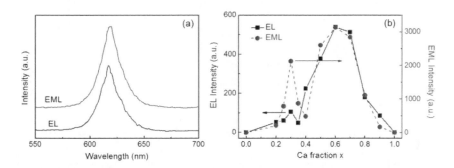

Figure 7. (a) EL and EML spectra of $(Ba, Ca)TiO_3:Pr^{3+}$ excited by electric field and stress, respectively. (b) EL- and EML-intensity dependences on the Ca composition of $Ba_{1-x}Ca_xTiO_3:Pr^{3+}$.

Diphase $Ba_{1-x}Ca_xTiO_3:Pr^{3+}$ in the range of x=0.25-0.90 consists of Ba-rich piezoelectric phase $Ba_{0.77}Ca_{0.23}TiO_3:Pr^{3+}$ and Ca-rich phosphor phase

$Ba_{0.1}Ca_{0.9}TiO_3:Pr^{3+}$. The spectral peaks of EL and EML are identical and located at 617 nm, as shown in Figure 7(a), and both come from the $^1D_2$-$^3H_4$ transition of Pr^{3+} in the phosphor phase. Figure 7(b) presents the Ca composition dependences of the EL- and EML-intensity. Similar variations for the EL- and EML- intensity with the Ca concentration are obviously observed. The well consistence indicates that the EL and EML behaviors are closely related.

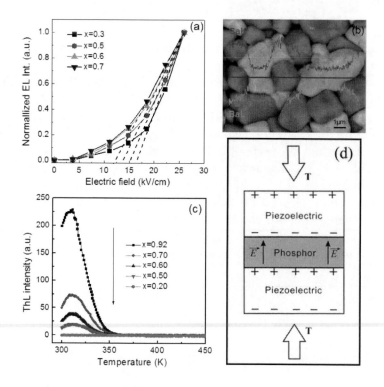

Figure 8. (a) Electric field threshold of EL for diphase Ba1-xCaxTiO3:Pr3+ (x=0.3, 16.4 kV/cm; x=0.5, 15 kV/cm; x=0.6, 13.6 kV/cm; x=0.7, 12 kV/cm). (b) BSEM image and EDS line-scan spectrum of diphase (Ba, Ca)TiO3:Pr3+. (blue, scan trace; red, Ca distribution; green, Ba distribution). (c) Thermoluminescence (ThL) curves of Ba1-xCaxTiO3:Pr3+ (x=0.2, 0.5, 0.6, 0.7, and 0.92). (d) Schematic diagram of EML for diphase (Ba, Ca)TiO3:Pr3+ with sandwich structure.

The electric field dependence of the EL intensity for diphase ceramic samples is given in Figure 8(a). They show a very flat increase in brightness at low electric field, and a faster increase when electric field exceeds a threshold

(16.4, 15, 13.6, and 12 kV/cm for the samples with x=0.3, 0.5, 0.6, and 0.7, respectively), above which the curves stretch along the electric field axis. Figure 8(b) illuminates the backscattered scanning electron microscopy (BSEM) and energy dispersive X-ray spectroscopy (EDS) of diphase (Ba, Ca)TiO$_3$:Pr^{3+}. The light grains are Ba-rich piezoelectric phase Ba$_{0.77}$Ca$_{0.23}$TiO$_3$:Pr^{3+} and dark grains are Ca-rich phosphor phase Ba$_{0.1}$Ca$_{0.9}$TiO$_3$:Pr^{3+}, which is confirmed by the EDS line-scan spectrum. It is obviously observed that the two phases combine strongly on the nano- and micrometer scales and the phosphor grains are tightly sandwiched by the piezoelectric grains in three dimensions. Figure 8(c) shows the thermoluminescence (ThL) curves of Ba$_{1-x}$Ca$_x$TiO$_3$:Pr^{3+}. There is no ThL peak for the x=0.2 sample, i.e. Ba-rich piezoelectric phase. However, the ThL peak at around 311 K gradually enhances with the content increase of Ca-rich phosphor phase. These results indicate that the trap levels exist in the phosphor phase. According to the above investigation, a schematic diagram of EML for diphase (Ba, Ca)TiO$_3$:Pr^{3+} with sandwich structure is proposed. The electric field E induced by the piezoelectric effect of piezoelectric phase under the compressive load of 1000 N is calculated. The value of E is about 20 kV/cm, which is much higher than the above-mentioned EL thresholds [Figure 8(a)]. It indicates that the piezoelectric field is large enough to induce EL.

Therefore, the EML mechanism of diphase (Ba, Ca)TiO$_3$:Pr^{3+} can be explained by the piezoelectrically induced EL model. When the mechanical pressure is applied, a piezoelectric field will be applied on the phosphor due to the piezoelectric effect. The carriers (electrons) trapped in phosphor under the local piezoelectric field are released and accelerated to impact and excite Pr^{3+}. This model has also been used to discuss the EML mechanism of ZnAl$_2$O$_4$:Mn^{2+} [31], SrAl$_2$O$_4$:Eu^{2+} [33,34], and ZnS:Mn^{2+} [34].

4.2. Piezoelectrically Induced Carriers De-Trapping Model

However, it is difficult to experimentally confirm above-mentioned scenario on EML. Furthermore, EML also occurs under the load which is much weaker than 1000 N. For example, the EML threshold load of diphase (Ba, Ca)TiO$_3$:Pr^{3+} is only 350 N [28]. The piezoelectric field induced by the weak stress seems too weak to make the carries obtain enough energy to impact luminescent centers. Therefore, some researchers proposed the piezoelectrically induced trapped carrier de-trapping model. The piezoelectric field induced by mechanical stimulus causes decrease in the trap-depth. The trapped carriers (electrons or holes) de-trap from the traps and transfer to shallower traps, and then recombine with the luminescence centers, resulting in photon emission. Take $CaZr(PO_4)_2:Eu^{2+}$ for example, the EML model is analyzed [25].

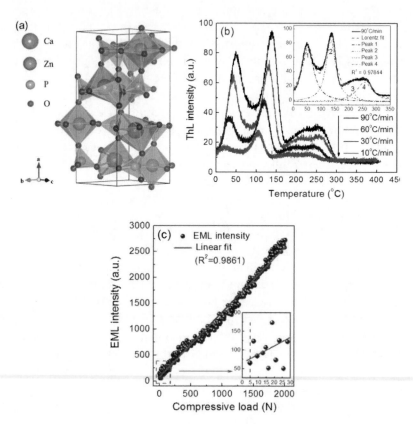

Figure 9. (a) Crystal structure of $CaZr(PO_4)_2$. (b) ThL curves of the $CaZr(PO_4)_2:Eu^{2+}$ phosphor at different heating rates. (Inset) The fitting curves of ThL spectrum at the heating rate of 90 °C/min. (c) Typical EML linear behavior of $CaZr(PO_4)_2:Eu^{2+}$ during application of load up to 2000 N.

Figure 9(a) shows the crystal structure of $CaZr(PO_4)_2$, which belongs to the orthorhombic system with symmetry class 222 and space group $P2_12_12_1$, Z = 4 (a=14.488 Å, b=6.721 Å, c=6.235 Å). Of the 32 crystal classes, 20 exhibit direct piezoelectricity. These classes are: 1; 2; m; 222; mm2; 4; $\overline{4}$; 422; 4mm; $\overline{4}$2m; 3; 32; 3m; 6; $\overline{6}$; 622; 6mm; $\overline{6}$2m; 23; $\overline{4}$3m. It is obviously that the space group 222 of $CaZr(PO_4)_2$ belongs to one of the 20 piezoelectric classes. The piezoelectricity of the host material provides a prerequisite for the EML in $CaZr(PO_4)_2:Eu^{2+}$. Figure 9(b) shows the ThL curves of $CaZr(PO_4)_2:Eu^{2+}$ irradiated by 254 nm UV light for 1 min. There exist several ThL peaks for each ThL curve. In the ThL glow curve, each peak represents one type of trap centers present in the system. The existence of different ThL peaks indicates that there are several kinds of traps in this material. The sub-peak fitting of ThL curves indicate that each ThL curve can be well separated to four peaks using Lorentz fit [inset of Figure 9(b)], suggesting four types of traps in the $CaZr(PO_4)_2:Eu^{2+}$ phosphor. According to the Hoogenstraaten method [35], the depths of trap levels are derived $E_t = 0.687$ eV (Peak 1), 0.829 eV (Peak 2), 1.171 eV (Peak 3) and 1.873 eV (Peak 4) for different kinds of traps, respectively. Figure 9(c) displays the typical EML linear behavior of $CaZr(PO_4)_2:Eu^{2+}$ during application of compressive load up to 2000 N. The increase in compressive load induces a corresponding linear increase in EML intensity.

There are two superiorities of EML in $CaZr(PO_4)_2:Eu^{2+}$. Firstly, the load threshold for the EML in $CaZr(PO_4)_2:Eu^{2+}$ is only 4.86 N, much lower than that of $(Ba,Ca)TiO_3:Pr^{3+}$ (350 N). Secondly, EML from $CaZr(PO_4)_2:Eu^{2+}$ could be excited by a broad dynamic range of compressive force. The EML reaches an unsaturated peak value even for the excited load up to 2000 N, showing the trend of sustained growth. It is much higher than the previously reported peak load of other EML materials, e.g. $Sr_3Sn_2O_7:Sm^{3+}$ (250 N) [22] and $(Ba,Ca)TiO_3:Pr^{3+}$ (1000 N) [28,29].

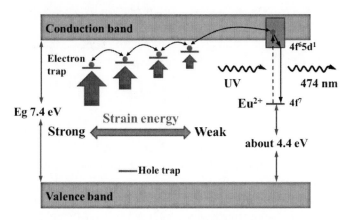

Figure 10. Schematic diagram of EML process for $CaZr(PO_4)_2:Eu^{2+}$.

On the basis of these results and previous works [12,19,24,28,36-38], EML is explained with the piezoelectrically induced trapped carrier de-trapping model, as shown in Figure 10. When $CaZr(PO_4)_2:Eu^{2+}$ is irradiated with UV light (254 nm), the electrons are firstly excited from the $4f^7$ ground level of Eu^{2+} to $4f^65d^1$ level. Because the 5d levels of Eu^{2+} are partly in the conduction band of $CaZr(PO_4)_2$, some electrons can escape to the conduction band with the aid of thermal energy (i.e. lattice vibrations) or photoexcitation energy. Eu^{2+} stays now as $Eu^{2+}-h^+$. Then the electron is trapped from the conduction band to an electron trap (V_O or $[Eu_{Ca}]^+$) and migrate from one trap to another with the aid of acquiring (or releasing) thermal energy. When a stress is applied, the $CaZr(PO_4)_2:Eu^{2+}$ lattice is deformed, inducing a strain energy and generating a local electric field in the piezoelectric region, and then these trapped electrons are de-trapped. Electrons in the shallow trap levels could be excited to the conduction band by the weak strain energy, while under the strong strain energy electrons in the deep trap levels could be excited to shallower contiguous trap levels, then to the conduction band, or directly to the conduction band by tunneling. The de-trapped electrons subsequently come back to the 5d levels of $Eu^{2+}-h^+$. Finally, the relaxation of the electrons back to the ground level of Eu^{2+} produces a cyan light emission (474 nm).

5. ELASTICO-MECHANOLUMINESCENT APPLICATIONS

At present, EML has shown important applications in many fields, including stress sensor, real-time visualization of stress distribution, determination of ultrasonic powers, structural health diagnosis, light source, bio-imaging, and so on. Some applications of EML are introduced in following parts.

5.1. Stress Sensor

EML can realize the energy transfer from mechanical stress to luminescence. Several EML materials response to various stresses, such as touch, impact, vibration, friction, stretching, compression, bend, and twist. Therefore, the multi-stress sensitive coating including EML particles can be used as artificial skin [6] or touch sensor [24] to sense mechanical stress.

5.2. Stress Distribution Detecting

The most impressive and widespread application of stress-sensitive coating is to detect stress distribution. The technique is based on the accurate linear relation between EML intensity and various stress parameters, especially for the stress intensity. Hence, the EML brightness distribution reflects the stress distribution. This stress distribution visualization technology could be used to non-destructively decipher the stress distribution of dynamic moving parts, such as artificial bones [39], machine parts [3,5], and other objects [27].

5.3. Structural Health Diagnosis

In addition to detecting the stress in the process of elastic deformation, EML particles can also be used as the stress probes to real-time visualize the internal defect in solids, such as visualization of internal defect in a pipe [40], visualization of active crack on bridge and building [41], real-time visualization of the quasidynamic crack-propagation in ceramics or concrete [42], and determination of the crack-growth resistance and other parameters of crack-propagation [43].

5.4. Light Source

EML is one of pump light sources, for example, EML materials with UV or blue light emission can excite other phosphors, such as fluorescent dye [44]. Single EML particle can also be used as ubiquitous light source with controllable intensity in nW order [45].

Furthermore, by regulating the mixing ratio of two EML materials with different emissions, such as ZnS: Cu, Mn (orange) and ZnS: Cu (green), a warm white light or a patterned multicolored image could be obtained using EML [46-48]. Therefore, an incandescent lamp can be substituted with EML composite films with highly brightness and durability. The EML is environmentally friendly because light can be generated by way of a naturally vibrating phenomenon (e.g. wind).

5.5. Bio-Imaging

Near infra-red (NIR) fluorescence bio-imaging (FBI) is one of the key technologies for the biomedical sciences. It is used for the imaging of biological substances, and can also be utilized in techniques involving fluorescence immunoassay, photo dynamic therapy, and drug delivery systems. EML materials can emit light upon the application of mechanical stress or ultrasonic wave excitation, a nondestructive and noninvasive stimulation technique used for biotissues. Therefore, in order to realize the application of EML bio-imaging, EML materials with NIR emission have been developed, such as $SrAl_2O_4:Eu^{2+}$, Er^{3+} with a 1530 nm emission [23].

6. CHALLENGES AND PERSPECTIVES

The number of EML materials is relatively limited. The research on EML is in the primary phase. There is no unanimous system to evaluate the performance of EML materials. Many EML materials (while possibly working in the lab) cannot be used in practice, which drives the search for new materials with good performance. However, the design and manufacture of EML materials are still largely based on the experience of researchers. It is urgent to explore the design principle of EML materials. Other issues that are critical with respect to biological and medical applications include the tendency towards fouling and cellular toxicity in general.

The EML mechanism is still ambiguous, without unified viewpoint. It is well known that EML materials belong to piezoelectrically defect-controlled type of luminescent materials. However, the effects of crystal structure and trap levels on the EML performance are discussed only from the experimental phenomena. Furthermore, the origin and properties of traps which participate in the EML process represent another challenge.

ACKNOWLEDGMENTS

This work was supported by Shandong Provincial Natural Science Foundation, China (ZR2013EMQ003), the Program of Science and Technology in Qingdao City (13-1-4-195-jch), the Natural Science Foundation of China (51072136 and 51373082), the Shandong Provincial Natural Science

Foundation for Distinguished Young Scholars (JQ201103), the Taishan Scholars Program of Shandong Province (ts20120528), and the Program for Scientific Research Innovation Team in Colleges and Universities of Shandong Province.

REFERENCES

[1]   J. Walton, Triboluminescence, *Adv. Phys.* 26, 887 (1977).

[2]   B. P. Chandra and A. S. Rathore, Classification of mechanoluminescence, *Cryst. Res. Technol.* 30, 885 (1995).

[3]   C. N. Xu, "Coatings", in Encyclopedia of Smart Materials, edited by M. Schwartz (Wiley, New York, USA, 2002), vol. 1, p. 190-201.

[4]   B. P. Chandra, *Mechanoluminescence*, in *Luminescence of Solids*, ed. D. R. Vij (Plenum Press, 1988), pp. 361.

[5]   C. N. Xu, T. Watanabe, M. Akiyama and X. G. Zheng, Direct view of stress distribution in solid by mechanoluminescence, *Appl. Phys. Lett.* 74, 2414 (1999).

[6]   C. N. Xu, T. Watanabe, M. Akiyama and X. G. Zheng, Artificial skin to sense mechanical stress by visible light emission, *Appl. Phys. Lett.* 74, 1236 (1999).

[7]   Hiroaki Matsui, Chao-Nan Xu, Morito Akiyama, and Tadahiko Watanabe, Strong mechanoluminescence from UV-irradiated spinels of $ZnGa_2O_4$:Mn and $MgGa_2O_4$:Mn, *Jpn. J. Appl. Phys.* 39, 6582 (2000).

[8]   H. Matsui, C. N. Xu, and H. Tateyama, Stress-stimulated luminescence from $ZnAl_2O_4$:Mn, *Appl. Phys. Lett.* 78, 1068 (2001).

[9]   Morito Akiyama, Chao-Nan Xu, and Kazuhiro Nonaka, Intense visible light emission from stress-activated ZrO_2:Ti, *Appl. Phys. Lett.* 81, 457 (2002).

[10] M. Akiyama, C. N. Xu, H. Matsui, K. Nonaka and T. Watanabe, Recovery phenomenon of mechanoluminescence from $Ca_2Al_2SiO_7$:Ce by irradiation with ultraviolet light, *Appl. Phys. Lett.* 75, 2548 (1999).

[11] X. Wang, C. N. Xu, H. Yamada, K. Nishikubo and X. G. Zheng, Electro-mechano-optical conversions in Pr^{3+}-doped $BaTiO_3$-$CaTiO_3$ ceramics, *Adv. Mater.* 17, 1254 (2005).

[12] H. W. Zhang, H. Yamada, N. Terasaki and C. N. Xu, Ultraviolet mechanoluminescence from $SrAl_2O_4$:Ce and $SrAl_2O_4$:Ce,Ho, *Appl. Phys. Lett.* 91, 081905 (2007).

[13] L. Zhang, H. Yamada, Y. Imai and C. N. Xu, Observation of elasticoluminescence from $CaAl_2Si_2O_8$:Eu^{2+} and its water resistance behavior, *J. Electrochem. Soc.* 155, J63 (2008).

[14] H. W. Zhang, H. Yamada, N. Terasaki and C. N. Xu, Green mechanoluminescence of $Ca_2MgSi_2O_7$:Eu and $Ca_2MgSi_2O_7$:Eu,Dy, *J. Electrochem. Soc.* 155, J55 (2008).

[15] H. W. Zhang, H. Yamada, N. Terasaki and C. N. Xu, Blue light emission from stress-activated $CaYAl_3O_7$:Eu, *J. Electrochem. Soc.* 155, J128 (2008).

[16] N. Madhusudhana Rao, D. Raja Reddy, B. K. Reddy, and C. N. Xu, Intense red mechanoluminescence from $(ZnS)_{1-x}(MnTe)_x$, *Phys. Lett. A*, 372 4122 (2008).

[17] H. Zhang, H. Yamada, N. Terasaki and C. N. Xu, Stress-induced mechanoluminescence in $SrCaMgSi_2O_7$:Eu, *Electrochem. Solid-State Lett.* 10, J129 (2007).

[18] L. Zhang, C. N. Xu, and H. Yamada, Strong mechanoluminescence from oxynitridosilicate phosphors, *IOP Conf. Series: Materials Science and Engineering* 18, 212001 (2011).

[19] J. Botterman, K. V. D. Eeckhout, I. D. Baere, D. Poelman and P. F. Smet, Mechanoluminescence in $BaSi_2O_2N_2$:Eu, *Acta Mater.* 60, 5494 (2012).

[20] H. Zhang, C. N. Xu, N. Terasaki and H. Yamada, Electro-mechano-optical luminescence from $CaYAl_3O_7$:Ce, *Electrochem. Solid-State Lett.* 14, J76 (2011).

[21] S. Kamimura, H. Yamada and C. N. Xu, Development of new elasticoluminescent material $SrMg_2(PO_4)_2$:Eu, *J. Lumin.* 132, 526 (2012).

[22] S. Kamimura, H. Yamada and C. N. Xu, Strong reddish-orange light emission from stress-activated $Sr_{n+1}Sn_nO_{3n+1}$:Sm^{3+} (n=1, 2, ∞) with perovskite-related structures, *Appl. Phys. Lett.* 101, 091113 (2012).

[23] Y. Terasawa, C. N. Xu, H. Yamada and M. Kubo, Near infra-red mechanoluminescence from strontium aluminate doped with rare-earth ions, *IOP Conf. Series: Materials Science and Engineering* 18, 212013 (2011).

[24] J. C. Zhang, C. N. Xu, S. Kamimura, Y. Terasawa, H. Yamada and X. Wang, An intense elastico-mechanoluminescence material $CaZnOS$:Mn^{2+} for sensing and imaging multiple mechanical stresses, *Opt. Express* 21, 12976 (2013).

[25] J. C. Zhang, C. N. Xu and Y. Z. Long, Elastico-mechanoluminescence in $CaZr(PO_4)_2:Eu^{2+}$ with multiple trap levels, *Opt. Express* 21, 13699 (2013).

[26] X. Fu, H. Yamada, and C. N. Xu, Property of highly oriented $SrAl_2O_4:Eu$ film on quartz glass substrates and its potential application in stress sensor, *J. Electrochem. Soc.* 156, J249 (2009).

[27] C. Li, C. N. Xu, Y. Imai, and N. Bu, Real-time visualisation of the Portevin-Le Chatelier effect with mechanoluminescent-sensing film, *Strain* 47, 483 (2011).

[28] J. C. Zhang, X. Wang, X. Yao, C. N. Xu and H. Yamada, Strong elastico-mechanoluminescence in diphase $(Ba,Ca)TiO_3:Pr^{3+}$ with self-assembled sandwich architectures, *J. Electrochem. Soc.* 157, G269 (2010).

[29] J. C Zhang, M. Tang, X. Wang, Y. Li, and X. Yao, Elastico-mechanoluminescence properties of Pr^{3+}-doped $BaTiO_3$-$CaTiO_3$ diphase ceramics with water resistance behavior, *Ceram. Int.* 38S, S581 (2012).

[30] Y. Liu and C. N. Xu, Electroluminescent ceramics excited by low electrical field, *Appl. Phys. Lett.* 84, 5016 (2004).

[31] H. Matsui, C. N. Xu, Y. Liu and H. Tateyama, Origin of mechanoluminescence from Mn-activated $ZnAl_2O_4$: Triboelectricity-induced electroluminescence, *Phys. Rev. B* 69, 235109 (2004).

[32] J. C. Zhang, X. Wang, X. Yao, C. N. Xu, and H. Yamada, Studies on ac electroluminescence device made of $BaTiO_3$-$CaTiO_3:Pr^{3+}$ diphase ceramics, *Appl. Phys. Express* 3, 022601 (2010).

[33] H. Yamada, H. Kusaba, and C. N. Xu, Anisotropic lattice behavior in elasticoluminescent material $SrAl_2O_4:Eu^{2+}$, *Appl. Phys. Lett.* 92, 101909 (2008).

[34] V. K. Chandra, B. P. Chandra, and P. Jha, Strong luminescence induced by elastic deformation of piezoelectric crystals, *Appl. Phys. Lett.* 102, 241105 (2013).

[35] W. Hoogenstraaten, Electron traps in zinc-sulfide phosphors, *Philips Res. Rep.* 13, 515 (1958).

[36] K. Korthout, K. Van den Eeckhout, J. Botterman, S. Nikitenko, D. Poelman, and P. F. Smet, Luminescence and x-ray absorption measurements of persistent $SrAl_2O_4:Eu,Dy$ powders: evidence for valence state changes, *Phys. Rev. B* 84, 085140 (2011).

[37] H. Yamamoto and T. Matsuzawa, Mechanism of long phosphorescence of $SrAl_2O_4:Eu^{2+},Dy^{3+}$ and $CaAl_2O_4:Eu^{2+},Nd^{3+}$, *J. Lumin.* 72-74, 287 (1997).

[38] V. K. Chandra, B. P. Chandra, and P. Jha, Models for intrinsic and extrinsic elastico and plasticomechanoluminescence of solids, *J. Lumin.* 138, 267 (2013).

[39] K. Hyodo, Y, Terasawa, C. N. Xu, H. Sugaya, and S. Miyakawa, Mechanoluminescent stress imaging for hard tissue biomechanics, *J. Biomech.* 45, S263 (2012).

[40] C. N. Xu, N. Ueno, N. Terasaki, and H. Yamada, Mechanoluminescence and novel structural health diagnosis (Book Style), NTS, Tokyo, 2012.

[41] N. Terasaki, C. N. Xu, C. Li, L. Zhang, C. Z. Li, D. Ono, M. Tsubai, Y. Adachi, Y. Imai, N. Ueno, and T. Shinokawa, Visualization of active crack on bridge in use by mechanoluminescent sensor, *Proc. of SPIE* 8348, 83482D (2012).

[42] J. S. Kim, H. J. Koh, W. D. Lee, N. Shin, J. G. Kim, K. H. Lee, and K. S. Sohn, Quasi-dynamic visualization of crack propagation and wake evolution in Y-TZP ceramic by mechano-luminescence, *Met. Mater. Int.* 14, 165 (2008).

[43] J. S. Kim, K. Kibble, Y. N. Kwon, and K. S. Sohn, Rate-equation model for the loading-rate-dependent mechanoluminescence of $SrAl_2O_4:Eu^{2+}$, Dy^{3+}, *Opt. Lett.* 34, 1915 (2009).

[44] N. Terasaki, H. Zhang, H. Yamada, and C. N. Xu, Mechanoluminescent light source for a fluorescent probe molecule, *Chem. Commun.* 47, 8034 (2011).

[45] N. Terasaki and C. N. Xu, Performance of single mechanoluminescent particle as ubiquitous light source, *J. Colloid Interface Sci.* (2013), http://dx.doi.org/10.1016/j.jcis.2013.11.070

[46] S. M. Jeong, S. Song, S. K. Lee, and B. Choi, Mechanically driven light-generator with high durability, *Appl. Phys. Lett.* 102, 051110 (2013).

[47] S. M. Jeong, S. Song, K. I. Joo, J, Jeong, and S. H. Chung, Bidirectional two colored light emission from stress-activated ZnS-microparticles-embedded polydimethylsiloxane elastomer films, *Opt. Mater. Express* 3, 1600 (2013).

[48] S. M. Jeong, S. Song, S. K. Lee, and N. Y. Ha, Color manipulation of mechanoluminescence from stress-activated composite films, *Adv. Mater.* 25, 6194 (2013).

In: Advances in Optoelectronics Research   ISBN: 978-1-63321-211-4
Editor: Marcus R. Oswald   © 2014 Nova Science Publishers, Inc.

Chapter 4

NONLINEAR AND FLUCTUATION PHENOMENA UNDER CONDITIONS OF STRONG SELECTIVE REFLECTION IN INCLINED GEOMETRY

Ya. A. Fofanov

Institute for Analytical Instrumentation RAS., St.-Petersburg, Russia

ABSTRACT

This chapter is devoted to investigation of the strong selective reflection of an obliquely incident laser beam (inclined geometry) from the interface "glass - rubidium vapour". Passages from the resonance Brewster reflection to the resonantly frustrated total internal reflection (TIR), caused by the frequency tuning of the incident radiation, are demonstrated experimentally. The intensity of the reflected light at these passages changes in more than 20 times. The contrast of the strongest reflection resonances exceeds 500% at the moderate heating of reflecting cells. A simple theory, which is based on a two-level model for resonance atoms and Fresnel formulas for reflection coefficients, is presented. Numerical calculations based on the proposed theory confirm main experimental results.

The controlling of the intensity and fluctuations of the selective reflected light was also investigated at the optical saturation of the resonance transitions. The relative reduction of the intensity fluctuations is recorded in reflected light compared with the incident one. It is shown also that the optical saturation of selective reflection resonances leads to the appearance in the reflection spectra of new nonlinear structures. On conditions of frustrated TIR the asymmetry of saturation of hyperfine components D2-line in a natural abundance of rubidium isotopes is registered.

The noise of single-mode semiconductor laser with an external optical feedback is studied. The totally single-mode quantum lasing (TSQL) with a complete suppression of all system of subthreshold modes, including the subthreshold side modes of the laser's own cavity and the noisy modes of the external cavity is theoretically predicted and experimentally realized. The realized TSQL is characterized by a squeezed photon fluctuations in comparison with classical (coherent) light.

The selective reflection spectra are described where the frequency of lasing mode of the used semiconductor laser was jumplike retuned over the modes of the external (long) cavity. In this case, the characteristic steps—intensity quasilevels—arise on the reflectivity resonances. Low-noise reflectivity regimes with different sensitivities to external signals are found on these quasilevels.

In the final part of the chapter the possibility of reducing the quantum fluctuations for selectively reflected light on conditions of optical saturation of resonance transitions is explored. The single-mode semiconductor laser with external cavity has been used as a light source. When the laser is tuned according to the quasilevels, which have minimum intrinsic noise, the squeezing of amplitude quantum fluctuations of the selectively reflected radiation relative to the incident coherent light has been recorded.

The investigations in this chapter complement the optoelectronics, classical and quantum optics, and they can be useful for the further development of these disciplines.

1. INTRODUCTION

The selective reflection (SR) i.e. the reflection from the dielectric - resonant atomic gas interface is known for a long time [1-3]. The interest in this phenomenon was related mainly to its applications for the spectroscopy, especially the spectroscopy of dense gases [2, 4-7]. Strong impulse for the study and application of the SR was done by the finding of sub-Doppler resonances [3, 8-15]. Selective reflection is also a good method for studies of the interaction of excited atoms with a solid surface including van der Waals interaction [16-18]. One of the useful applications of SR is the stabilization of the laser frequency [19-22].

There are two basic schemes that are used to study the SR: traditional single beam scheme (SB-scheme) [1-17], and pump-probe scheme (PP-scheme) that use pump and probe beams with independent frequencies [18, 23-28]. Selective reflection is investigated in a wide range from normal up to large light incidence angles [29, 30]. Additional advantages are provided under investigation on conditions of total internal reflection (TIR) because the interaction atoms with evanescent wave takes place at the vicinity of dielectric surface [30-34]. The study of nonlinear SR reveals some important new details of the resonant interaction of atoms and fields near the interface [13, 23, 29, 35-38]. The novel features and prospects of development of the high sensitive laser spectroscopy has recently made possible with intensive investigations of SR as compare with transmission in "nanometric" gas cells (super-thin cells) [39-41].

Separately, it is noted that the use of semiconductor lasers (diode lasers) is proved quite effective for the study of SR [11, 35]. In PP-scheme the lasers diode are often used in combination with the lasers of other types [25, 27]. The relatively high level of frequency fluctuations (phase noise) of semiconductor lasers was helpful for the development of diode lasers noise spectroscopy [35, 42]. More detailed fluctuations (including quantum ones) of lasers diode as well as their use for the spectroscopy, precision optical measurements, and investigations of SR, are considered in [43-47].

In this chapter are described the studies of the novel nonlinear and fluctuation phenomena under strong SR from the interface "glass - rubidium vapour" in an inclined geometry.

2. EXPERIMENTAL TECHNIQUE

All of the investigations described in this chapter are carried out with SB-scheme. Generalized scheme of the experimental setup is shown in Figure 1 [48,49]. As the radiation source is used a single-frequency semiconductor laser (λ = 780 nm) with Fabry-Perot cavity. The adjustment of laser frequency is performed by control the injection current. The laser radiation is directed on the reflection and absorbing cells by means of beam splitter BS. Both cells are filled with natural abundance of [85]Rb and [87]Rb isotopes. In reflection cell laser radiation interacts with a glass - rubidium vapor interface. The orientation of the polarization plane of incident laser radiation is set using polarizer P. Laser radiation is detected by photodiodes PD1, PD2, and then the absorption and reflection signals are transmitted in the registration system. Lenses L1, L2 are designed for focusing the laser radiation on the surface to be studied, and for matching parameters of the reflected beam with an aperture of the photodetector. Absorption signal is used for the calibration of the laser frequency.

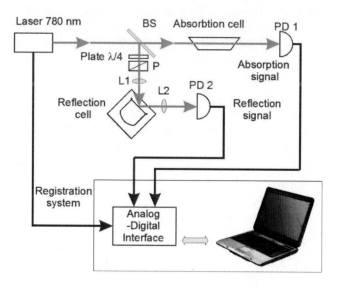

Figure 1. Experimental setup.

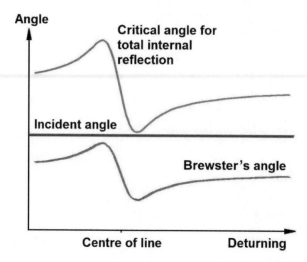

Figure 2. Critical and Brewster`s angels for SR.

entation is several times smaller than the corresponding
ient for the orthogonal orientation. This can be explained by
nditions at the bottom of dips in Figure 3 are approaching to
eas in the case of orthogonal polarization as is well known,
t.

ry Theoretical Model and Calculations

cal consideration is based on the model of a two-level atom
a plane light wave. It is assumed that the atom has only the
one excited state, no transitions occurs to other levels, and the
ion is not saturated by a laser field. On these assumptions the
wave vector k of a resonance light wave, which propagates
mble of atoms, is found (compare with [34]):

$$k'', \tag{1}$$

$$\Delta k'', \tag{2}$$

$$f/[\Gamma_{21}(1+\Delta\mu^2)], \tag{3}$$

concentration of atoms; f is the oscillator strength; Γ_{21} is the
half-width of the atomic line; $\Delta\mu = (\nu-\nu_a)/\Gamma_{21}$ is the
etuning of the field frequency ν from the atomic frequency ν_a,
nerical coefficient determined by fundamental constants and
m of units.
experimental situation, in which selective reflection was
four resonance lines, was described by calculating the total
wave vector

$$_i \Delta k_i, \tag{4}$$

On Figure 2 we can see the qualitative picture selective reflection of coherent light in inclined geometry. Light is polarized in the incidence plane (parallel polarization). The angle of incidence is determined only by the angular position of a reflecting cell. At the presence of a resonance gas, the critical angle of TIR and Brewster angle depend on the detuning of the optical frequency relative to the center of line. This leads to significant changes in the intensity of reflected light when adjusting the frequency. In particular a resonant approaching of the critical angle of TIR to the angle of incidence is accompanied by a sharp increase in the reflection coefficient.

3. LINEAR SR IN INCLINED GEOMETRY

3.1. Comparable Study of SR for Different Angles of Incidence and Polarizations

Figure 3 shows three typical dependences of the reflection coefficient R on the laser frequency (reflection spectra), which correspond to three different angles of incidence and the parallel polarization [48]. Figure 4 shows the relative intensity of light transmitted through the absorption cell (absorption spectrum). The hyperfine components of D2-lines of [85]Rb and [87]Rb isotopes (see inset on Figure 4) correspond to peaks a`, A`, B`, and b` in absorption spectra, which are used to calibrate frequency axes.

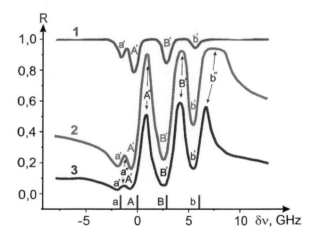

Figure 3. Experimental spectra of strong SR for parallel polarization.

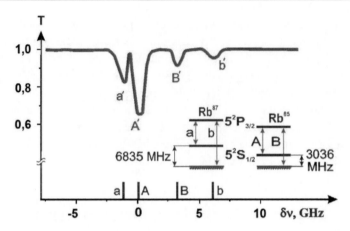

Figure 4. Absorption spectrum for Rubidium at 780 nm.

The shapes of reflection curves 1-3 in Figure 3 noticeably differ from each other. Reflection spectrum 1 corresponds to the angle of incidence 64° at which TIR conditions are fulfilled outside resonance lines or in the absence of Rb vapour because the nonresonance critical TIR angle is 34.6^O. One can see that curve 1 virtually coincides with the absorption curve: dips a`, A`, B`, and b` on the reflection spectrum 1 are similar to dips a`, A`, B`, and b` in absorption spectrum on Figure 4. This gives us the grounds for the suggestion that the dips in curves 1 are formed by the violation of TIR due to absorption in the resonance gas. More exactly radiation is scattered by atoms interacting with the evanescent wave existing under TIR conditions [29-34].

Reflection spectrum 2 in Figure 3 corresponds to the angle of incidence 34° at which TIR condition is not fulfilled outside resonance line (nonresonance R = 0.40). Curve 2 strongly differs from curve 1: the reflection coefficient at the bottom of dips a`, A`, B`, and b` are considerably decreased, but at the same time the reflection peaks a``, A``, B``, and b`` are appeared. The formation of reflection peaks is especially well observed by comparing peaks A``, B`` with peak b``. The top of peak b`` is still flat because at his frequency the conditions close to frustrated TIR is fulfilled. The reflection coefficient at the tops of peaks A`` and B`` are somewhat smaller, and these tops are sharper as compare with b``. Peaks a`` for all curves are weaker, that can be explained by the influence of neighbour peak A``.

Spectrum 3 in Figure 3 demonstrates pronounced resonance reflection in the inclined geometry. This spectrum corresponds to the angle of incidence 33° at which the reflection coefficient outside resonance lines is 0.10.

A comparison of spectra 2 and 3 shows th decrease with decreasing the angle of inc the deviation from conditions close to reflection coefficient at the top of peak B the contrast of this resonance (the ratio intensity) is no less than 5.

The resonance change in the refracti to the corresponding modification of th conditions approach to the Brewster ref BR because resonance gas has absorptio the angle of incidence the reflection co spectrum 3 in Figure 3 are much closer t result, the value of R drastically changes peaks to tops of them. This change for p 20 and 10, respectively.

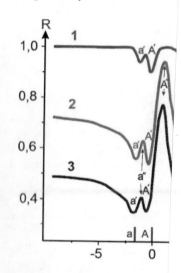

Figure 5. Experimental spectra of strong SF

Submitted in Figure 5 reflection the same characteristics as for the abov spectrum 1 is similar to the absorptior and 3 are retained the main features - the peaks A`` and B``. But there a reflection coefficient at the bottom of

---

the paral
reflection
that reflec
pseudo B
BR does n

3.2. Elem

The th
interacting
ground stat
resonance t
correction
through the

$$\Delta k = \Delta$$

$$\Delta k' = -$$

$$\Delta k'' = k$$

where n_0 is
homogeneou
dimensionles
and k_0'' is a
the chosen sy

The rea
determined b
correction to

$$\Delta k = \sum_{k=1}^{4}$$

where g_i is a factor taking into account the concentration ratio of rubidium isotopes and multiplicity of the levels [50,51]. It is assumed that the population of Zeeman and hyperfine sublevels is equilibrium.

Further by averaging over the Doppler distribution of atomic frequencies is determined the value of $<\Delta k>_D$, then the refractive index of the atomic gas is found:

$$n_2 = 1 + < \Delta k >_D /k, \tag{5}$$

The intensity reflection coefficients for parallel and orthogonal orientations of the polarization plane is determined by Fresnel formulas

$$R_\| = |\{(n_2/n_1)^2\cos \theta - [(n_2/n_1)^2 - \sin^2\theta]^{1/2}\}/ \\ \{(n_2/n_1)^2\cos \theta + [(n_2/n_1)^2 - \sin^2\theta]^{1/2}\}|^2, \tag{6}$$

$$R\perp = |\{\cos \theta - [(n_2/n_1)^2 - \sin^2\theta]^{1/2}\}/ \\ \{\cos \theta + [(n_2/n_1)^2 - \sin^2\theta]^{1/2}\}|^2, \tag{7}$$

where n_1 is the refractive index of the reflection cell window and θ is the angle of incidence (from cell window to the vapour).

The results of calculations for parallel and orthogonal orientations are presented in Figure 6 and Figure 7 respectively. To compare calculated and experimental results, the values of θ in (6) are selected for each of the curves in Figure 6 so that the theoretical values of the absorption coefficient at the bottom of dips B˘ in curve 1 and the reflection coefficient at maxima of peaks B`` in curves 2 and 3 coincided with the corresponding experimental values in curves 1-3 in Figure 3. The same values of θ are then substituted into (7) to construct each of the curves in Figure 7. This allows us to compare theoretical and experimental data obtained for both orientations of the polarization plane.

One can see that theoretical curves are in well agreement with experimental curves, demonstrating the high contrast and the great intensity of reflection resonances. The curves describing the reflection coefficients for light with the parallel polarization lie below the curves for the orthogonal polarization and the intensity of reflected light at the bottom of dips for the parallel polarization is considerably smaller. This confirms the existence of a resonance passage from nearly TIR to BR for light with the parallel orientation of the polarization plane.

Note that there exist differences between experimental and theoretical results. Thus, the width of the flat tops of peaks b`` on experimental curves 2 on Figure 3, 5 are noticeable smaller than that on calculated curves 2 on Figure 6, 7. In addition, on calculated curves 3 the maximum values of the reflection coefficient at peaks A`` are greater than at peaks b``, while in the experiments the situation is inverse. These and other similar discrepancies can be explained first of all by the simplicity of the used theoretical model. A detailed analysis requires the additional experimental date and more profound theoretical approaches [9, 18, 29, 37, 52-54]. This will probably make it possible to obtain from experimental data the new information on the interaction of atoms with resonance radiation near surfaces [16-18].

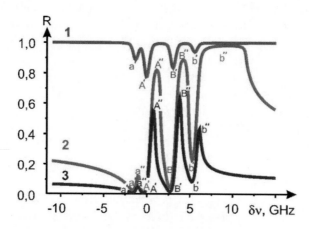

Figure 6. Calculated spectra of strong SR for parallel polarization.

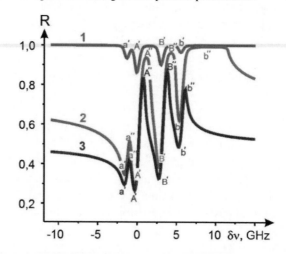

Figure 7. Calculated spectra of strong SR for orthogonal polarization.

3.3. Comparison with Similar Works

It is appropriate to compare the obtained results with the similar known works. In [5], a cell with mercury vapour was illuminated by the 253.5-nm radiation incident at the Brewster angle. In this case, the maximum selective reflection coefficient was 14 %. Strong reflection resonances in rubidium and cesium vapours at the angles of incidence close or equal to the Brewster angle were first observed in [30]. In the case of parallel orientation of the polarization plane in the presence of resonance atoms, the passage from BR to FTIR was observed. The reflection coefficient increased up to 95 % that exceeded the nonresonance reflection coefficient by an order of magnitude. Such a strong reflection was caused by high concentrations of atoms, which were achieved by heating a cell up to 350° C.

In this chapter, comparative investigations of resonance reflection from rubidium vapour were performed for light with parallel and orthogonal orientations of the polarization plane. By varying the angle of incidence, the initial (nonresonance) reflection conditions were controlled from TIR to conditions close to BR. At the angles of incidence exceeding the critical TIR angle, the violation of TIR was observed within a series of resonances for both polarizations, which was caused by the resonance absorption of coherent radiation by atoms interacting with a surface light wave.

If the angle of incidence for radiation with parallel polarization is chosen so that nonresonance reflection conditions were intermediate between TIR and BR, the tuning of laser is accompanied by the passages from reflection conditions close to selective (resonance) pseudo BR to conditions typical for selective (resonance) violated (failed, frustrated) TIR. At this passages, the intensity of the selective reflected light increases more than 20 times [48].

In [10], selective reflection from sodium vapour was investigated at low concentrations, when the homogeneous linewidth is smaller than the Doppler width. For the angle of incidence of 83°, the maximum reflection coefficient was ~ 77% and the contrast was 1.15. In our conditions, the contrast of the strongest reflection resonances exceeds five. This is approximately six times greater than in the case of sub-Doppler resonances in the orthogonal geometry at the same concentrations of resonance atoms [11]. In experiments described here, more than 60% of the incident light is reflected in strong maxima. To obtain comparable reflection in the orthogonal geometry, atomic concentrations should be a few orders higher [2]. At atomic concentrations comparable with these used in the present paper, the maximum reflection coefficient in the orthogonal configuration was 8% [11]. At the same time, the contrast of resonances that we observed was four times smaller than that in [30], which is explained by a lower concentration of resonance atoms in our study. In [34], the shift and broadening of the hyperfine structure of the D2-line in dense rubidium vapour were studied under frustrated TIR conditions.

Our studies have confirmed a significant increase in the amplitude of SR resonances for large incidence angles that had been observed previously in [30]. A contrast of the strongest refection resonances in SB-scheme exceeds 500% at the moderate heating of reflecting cell [48]. Our experiments showed no sub-Doppler resonances in the inclined geometry. Sub-Doppler reflection resonances in sodium vapour under TIR conditions observed in [32] were caused by the saturation of absorption and dispersion in a counterpropagating evanescence waves. The contrast of resonances was about 0.01 %. Reflection resonances described in the present chapter are a few orders stronger and are rather broad. This can be useful for solving other problems related, for example, to the transformation of light statistics. The negative influence of frequency fluctuations of probe laser radiation is noticeably reduced for broad reflection resonances, while the band of transmitted frequencies can be considerably broadened (see further this chapter and [55, 56]).

4. NONLINEAR SR IN INCLINED GEOMETRY

4.1. Saturation of the Strong SR

With increasing of the intensity of the laser radiation a resonant transitions as is well known, begins to saturate, that should affect the reflection. This subsection is devoted to the observation of the optical saturation of the strong SR. Fig.8 demonstrates the saturation of SR in inclined geometry that take place by increasing of surface power density W at the interface [49]. If the value of W is far from saturated, the linear reflection is realized, to which corresponds the reflection spectrum of W1. The angle of incidence for this spectrum is slightly smaller than the critical angle for TIR, and the light is polarized in the plane of incidence. The concentration of rubidium atoms is about 10^{15} cm^{-3}. The selective reflection of such tape is described in detailed in the above section.

Curves W2 and W3 in Fig.8 are obtained with a greater power density than curve W1. This increase of W achieved by means appropriate movement of the lens L1. One can clearly see the saturation of the observed selective reflection. As a result of the saturation the reflection curves become smoother. Particularly interesting that in passing from curve W1 to curve W3, the intensity of reflected light in maximum of the resonance A`` decreases approximately in 1.5 times.

The phenomenon of selective reflection saturation has been used to reduce the fluctuations of the reflected light [55, 56]. Indeed, the increase in surface power density occur not only during focusing, but also by increasing the intensity of the incident light. Due to the saturation, the relative increase in intensity of reflected light becomes smaller. In order experimental verification of this assumption between the BS and the laser has been set the intensity modulator (on Figure 1 is not shown). The laser is tuned on the top of the peak A``. Intensity of the laser radiation is modulated with modulation index of about several percents. It was found that in going from W1 to W3 in Figure 8, the modulation index of reflected light is reduced at 30% as compared to a modulation index of the incident light [55].

Thus, nonlinear resonance interface can operate as an original microcontroller (damper) intensity fluctuations of the reflected light. Further it will be shown that this microcontroller can also decrease the quantum fluctuations of selective reflected light.

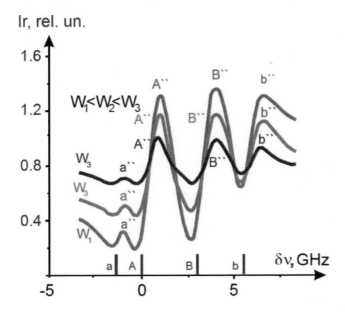

Figure 8. Optical saturation of the strong SR.

4.2. New Nonlinear Structures in SR Spectra

In this subsection we consider the new nonlinear structures that appear under conditions close to resonant TIR [49]. More detailed studies have shown also that the observed structures have the appearance of characteristic peaks on the tops of the reflection resonances. Depending on experimental conditions, are observed a series of peaks, as well as the single peaks.

The typical spectra showing the new non-linear structures, is presented in Figure 9. This spectrum meets the conditions of observation, close to the conditions for the curve W2 in Figure 8. Peaks P_1 and P_2 are good seen at the top of the resonance A``. At the tops of the resonances A`` and B`` begin to form a more weak peaks P_3 and P_4. Contrast of peaks P_1 and P_2 is about 1,5 %, the distance between peaks is about 150 MHz. Sufficiently good reproducibility of the spectra in Figure 9 can be seen from a comparison between two scans from a series of 20 ones, taken in the same experimental conditions.

In Figure 10 is shown an individual peak located on the components A``. More detailed image of this peak can be seen in inset on Figure 10. Contrast of this peak is about 6%. Its width is approximately 0.16 GHz. With a small change in the value W a similar nonlinear structure is also observed at the top of the resonance B`` [49].

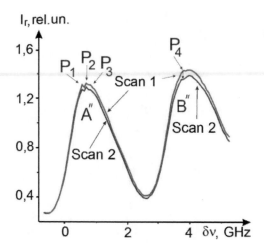

Figure 9. New nonlinear structures. Series of peaks.

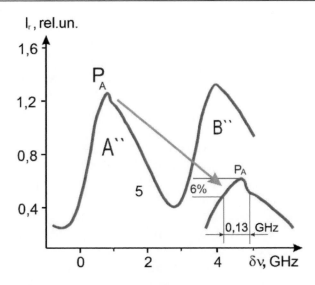

Figure 10. New nonlinear structures. Single peak.

Compare the obtained data with the known results and try to give the possible explanation of the nature of observed nonlinear phenomenon. One of the assumptions can be that the peaks in Figure 9, 10 are well known sub-Doppler resonances in SR [8-11]. However, it can not be so at least in several reasons. First, sub-Doppler resonances exist in zero detunings relative to the center of line, and only at angles of incidence close to the zero. Further, with an increasing of power density, these resonances begin to saturate [13, 29, 35-37].

Nonlinear structures described here, have not usual saturation properties. They are formed only in a fairly narrow range of values of the surface power density. Beside this, they appear at high angles and near the maxima of SR, which are strongly displaced relative to the centers of spectral lines. For example, the maximum resonance A`` of the reflection spectra in Figure 9, 10 is shifted of about 0.8 GHz in a high-frequency side from the center of the component A. Thus, the structures observed here are in no way can be associated with sub-Doppler resonances in SR, described in [8-15].

It seems appropriate to try to compare the observed here resonances with narrow Doppler-free resonances in SR under conditions of TIR that reported in [32]. And here we also are finding the same difference: these sub-Doppler resonances exist only at the centers of the corresponding optical transitions. The nature of these resonancies was discussed also in subsection 3.3.

Finally it should be noted external similarity of some features of the SR resonances describe here and the reflectance spectra of sub-micron thick vapor cell [39,40]. From the comparison of Figure 5 in [40] and Figure 10 in the present paper, we can see that in both cases the shapes of the peaks are very alike to each other. At the same time, here is the same important distinction - in the spectra of the SR from ultrathin cells the sub-Doppler resonances are observed at the central frequencies of optical transitions.

One of the possible explanations for the observed structures takes into account the existence of absorption in the resonance gas. This absorption leads to a gradual decrease in the intensity of transmitted light as it propagates from the interface. The result is a nonuniform optical saturation and therefore a spatial inhomogeneity of the gas refractive index near the window of the cell. As a consequence, the investigated interface can exhibit the optical properties similar in some respects to properties of ultrathin cells.

Some chance of success has also another assumption. It is based on the fact that the observed structures are associated with the manifestation in the system under investigation the properties of optical bistability [57]. The saturation of reflection leads to an increase the intensity of transmitted light. Because the resonance atoms are found in transmitted light, the increase of its intensity leads to further optical saturation of resonant gas and accordingly to the additional decrease of the reflection. Abrupt decline in the intensity on the right side of the peak in Figure 10 may be explained by the realization of this process.

Naturally, the above considerations can not be exhaustive. There can well be other assumptions (models) that in more detail consider all aspects of the resonant interaction of atoms with coherent radiation near the surface [16-18, 37, 57-59].

4.3. Asymmetry of Saturation of Selective TIR

This subsection is devoted to the study of another nonlinear phenomenon that is observed under conditions of TIR [60-61]. This phenomenon lies in the different rates of saturation of the hyperfine components a`, A`, B`, and b`. Reflectance spectra W1 - W3 shown in Figure 11, are obtained at the same angle of incidence, which was several degrees higher than the critical angle. In general, these spectra resemble the usual absorption spectrum (see Figure 4). The dashed line I_v gives the intensity of the light reflected from the interface glass – vacuum. The slope of this curve is determined by the well-known dependence of the intensity of the semiconductor laser from injection current [44]. The specified similarity of the reflection and absorption spectra is explained by the absorption of laser radiation in thin layer (evanescent wave) near the resonant interface. Since the absorption (more exactly scattering) occurs only at the resonance tuning of the laser, this phenomenon can also be called resonant frustrated (or violated) TIR.

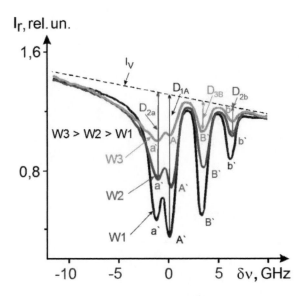

Figure 11. Asymmetry of saturation of selective TIR.

However, we note that there are several important differences between the spectra of W1 - W3 in Figure 11. The curve W1 corresponds to the linear reflection in which the surface power density W at the interface is much less than the saturating one. The spectra of W2 and W3 were obtained when the degree of focusing of the incident radiation was enough for saturation. Clearly seen, that the depth of the dips a`, A`, B`, and b` decreases with the growth of W. Herewith, one very important feature is well seen: the depth of the dip a` decreases slower, than the depth of the dips A`, B`, and b`. Another words, the component a` and the other hyperfine components become saturated with the different speed.

Consider this phenomenon in more detail. For this purpose we introduce the values St, which characterize the degree of saturation (decreasing depth of the dips) of the components a`, A`, B`, and b`: $St_{ia} = D_{1a}/D_{ia}$, $St_{iA} = D_{1A}/D_{iA}$, $St_{iB} = D_{1B}/D_{iB}$; and $St_{ib} = D_{1b}/D_{ib}$. Here D_{ia}, D_{iA}, D_{iB}, and D_{ib} – the depths of the dips a`, A`, B`, and b`; i = 1, 2, 3 in accordance with the numbering of curves W in Figure 11.

Figure 12 shows the values of St for each of the components of a `, A`, B `, and b` depending on the surface power density. The two areas are shown, which can be called "Identical saturation of a` and A`, B`, b`'" and "Different saturation of a` and A`, B`, b`'". As can be seen in the first area the components a `, A`, B`, and b` are saturated approximately the same.

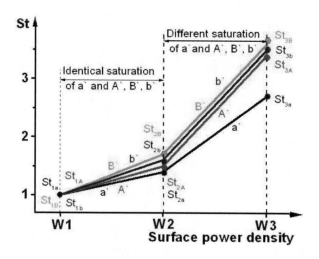

Figure 12. Identical and different saturation of a` and A`, B`, and b`.

In the area of "Different saturation of a` and A`, B`, b`'" the rates of saturation of the components A`, B`, and b` (the slope of the curves A`, B`, and b` in Figure 12) are equally increased: in the transition from W2 to W3 the values St_{iA}, St_{iB}, and St_{ib} are increased approximately 2.2 times. At the same time the value St_{ia} is increased approximately 1.8 times in the transition from W2 to W3, i.e. the component a` is saturated slower (more weakly).

A more detailed analysis shows that the component A` is also saturated little slower than the components of B` and b`. Thus, in the general case, there is the difference between the degree (velocity) of saturation of the components a`, A` and B`, b`. The described phenomenon can be called the asymmetry of saturation of selectively frustrated (disrupted) TIR.

Note that the separation into two regions of saturation and other reasoning here are quite approximate. Analytical separation of the components a` and A`, using the known methods of mathematical processing, is necessary, at least, for more thorough discussion. Nevertheless, the fact of slower saturation of a` in comparison with the other components in the area "Different saturation of a` and A`, B`, b`", remains obvious. This is clearly seen in Figure 11 without any mathematical processing.

A natural question arises: "Why is this happening?" One possible explanation for the observed asymmetry of saturation is based on the partial overlap of the inhomogeneously broadened components a` and A`, belonging to different isotopes of rubidium. Transitions a and A (see Figure 4) have the same oscillator strength, but the concentration of isotopes ^{85}Rb and ^{87}Rb in their natural mixture differs appreciably [50, 51]. This can lead to unequal quasi-resonant exchange of excitations at collisions between atoms ^{85}Rb and ^{87}Rb near the surface of the glass, and as a consequence, to the various degree (velocity) of saturation of components a` and A`, B`, b`.

5. QUASILEVELS OF INTENSITY OF SELECTIVE REFLECTED LIGHT

In this section we will continue discuss the possibility of transformation and control of the intensity and fluctuations of the selectively reflected light.

5.1. Saturation of Intensity Quasilevels

To continue research the experimental setup, used in the above sections, was modified as it is shown on Figure 13. Semiconductor laser (laser diode) is supplemented by external resonator formed with a diffraction grating G on a piezodrive PZT (see more detailed description in [56]). Driver contains the system stabilization and regulation of the injection current and temperature of the laser diode, as well as pozition of the diffraction grating, that provided the setting for the generation frequency on rubidium D2-line (λ = 780 nm). Laser radiation is reflected from the inner surface of the cell window filled with rubidium vapor, and is registered by the photodiode PD 1. The angle of incidence is slight less than critical angel for TIR.

Figure 14 gives the reflected light intensity as a function of increment δJ of injection current at the region of the reflective resonances A`` and B`` (compare with Figure 8). These curves are obtained under conditions where the position of the grating has been fixed and is scanned only the injection current. This resulted in the characteristic hoppings of the laser frequency according to the mode structure of the external cavity (see also subsection 6.1 and Figure 17). As a result, on the reflection spectra appeared typical steps - quasilevels of intensity. The width of quasilevels is given intermode distance, and their intensity is determined by the intensity of incident light and the reflection conditions [56].

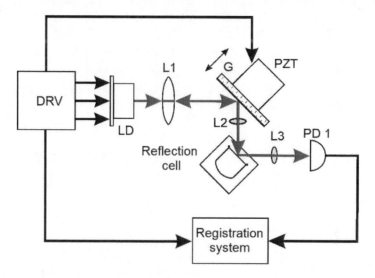

Figure 13. Setup for observation of intensity quasilevels.

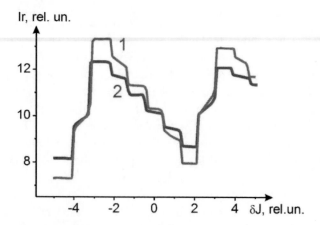

Figure 14. Quasilevels of intensity.

Curve 1 in Figure 14 corresponds to a linear reflection when the surface power density of the incident light is small as compared with the saturating. Curve 2 is taken at greater power density comparable to saturating. As can be seen, the optical saturation of reflection resonances leads to decrease in intensity of the quasilevels and thus the stabilizing properties of nonlinear resonance interface are saved during the formation of quasilevels. At the same time, changes in the slopes of the quasilevels can significantly modify their signal-noise characteristics. To verify this assumption the experiments are carried out as described in the next subsection.

5.2. Information Signals and Noise on Quasilevels

On Figure 15 is shown one of the characteristic dependences of the intensity of the reflected light observed with additional modulation of the injection current by an external generator (on Figure 13 is not shown). It can be seen that there appears the appropriate intensity modulation of quasilevels. The degree of modulation depends on both the concrete quasilevel and value of injection current within the quasilevel. On quasilevel located in the area of zero values of δJ, there is a significant suppression of the modulation signal: intensity modulation factor is reduced by more than ten times compared to neighboring quasilevels [56].

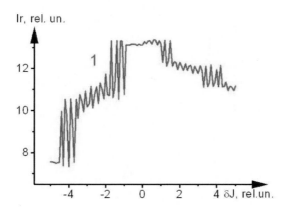

Figure 15. An information (modulation) signal on quasilevels.

During the study of the the noise level of quasilevels is carried out the spectral analysis of the signal PD 1 in Figure 13. Curve 1 in Figure 16 shows the characteristic dependence of the photocurrent fluctuations level from the value of δJ. It is clearly seen that the level of the intensity fluctuations depends on the concrete quasilevel and the position on the quasilevel. Noise level at Figure 16 is determined by two main factors: the actual fluctuations of the laser radiation intensity and the conversion of the fluctuations of the laser frequency in intensity noise occurring on quasilevels [38,42,62]. Moreover, the minimum noise level that shown in Figure 16, is comparable with the shot (photon) noise of the photodetection (shot-noise limit -SNL) [56].

The performed studies show, that there are certain possibilities of controlling the intensity and the fluctuations of the selectively reflected radiation of a semiconductor laser synchronized an external resonator. At the locking of the laser frequency by external cavity are formed the quasilevels of intensity, which height is determined, in particular, the degree of saturation of selective reflection resonances by the laser field. On quasilevels exist low-noise reflection modes having different sensitivities to external signals.

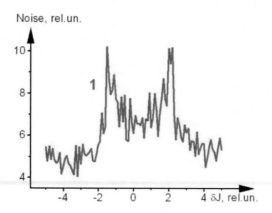

Figure 16. Noise of quasilevels.

6. THE NOISE OF A FABRY-PEROT SEMICONDUCTOR LASER WITH EXTERNAL OPTICAL FEEDBACK

6.1. Generation Spectrum and the Noise of a Semiconductor Laser

From the time they were first produced, semiconductor injection lasers based on heterojunctions (laser diodes) have been used to solve a very wide spectrum of fundamental and applied problems [63]. The intensive development of the technology for growing heterojunctions has led to the creation of single-mode semiconductor lasers with one well-developed lasing mode and adequate suppression of subthreshold (nonlasing) modes [44]. Later it has became clear that this type of laser has another remarkable property - it can be a source of sub-Poissonian light [64].

The emission spectrum of usual single-mode semiconductor laser with a Fabry-Perot cavity is shown in Figure 17-A. The characteristic frequency interval (intermode spacing) between the lasing and subthreshold (long-distance) modes, $\Delta v_{Int} = c/2L_{Int}$ is about 150 GHz. Here $L_{Int} \approx 1$ mm - is the optical path of an own cavity of a laser. In typical cases, the subthreshold modes are suppressed by about 20 dB by comparison with the lasing modes. Single-mode lasers that allow tuning to atomic lines are fairly widely used in spectroscopy and precision optical measurements [44].

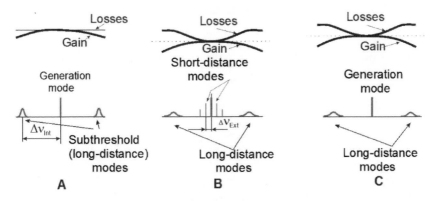

Figure 17. Mode structure of a semiconductor laser with external cavity.

Under certain conditions, due to the suppression of the shot noise of the injection current the excitation of the active medium of a semiconductor laser is not noisy. If excitation flux is efficiently converted by the laser into photons, the fluctuations of the generated photon-flux become sub-Poissonian, while the photodetection noise becomes lower than SNL. This phenomenon has attracted significant interest and has been repeatedly demonstrated experimentally [65-71].

However, it has turned out that the sub-Poissonian lasing of single-mode semiconductor lasers at room temperature is complicated by additional noise, introduced by competition with subthreshold side modes created by the laser's own cavity (long-distance modes, see Figure 17-A). As a result, the lasing mode, separated out, for example, by means of a monochromator or propagating in a medium with dispersion (a resonance atomic gas), will possess increased noise, despite the fact that the total radiation of the lasing and subthreshold modes can remain sub-Poissonian [43,67,72-76]. To obtain sub-Poissonian lasing for the principal mode, the side modes should be suppressed much more strongly that is ordinarily required [46].

6.2. Sub-Poissonian Lasing without Noise of All Subthreshold Modes

In a region free from low-frequency fluctuations and relaxation vibrations, the spectral noise power of the lasing mode of a single-mode semiconductor laser has the form [46, 47, 77].

$$F = \chi(1 + \xi), \tag{8}$$

where χ is the power of the intrinsic noise of the lasing mode with respect to the SNL:

$$\chi = (1/r)(2/r + 1); \tag{9}$$

ξ is the relative contribution introduced by competition of the lasing mode with one subthreshold mode; $F = (i^2)_{\Omega=0}/i$ is the Fano factor; i is the photocurrent; $r = (J - J_{th})/J_{th}$ the pump parameter, determined by the degree to which injection current J exceeds threshold current J_{th}.

In the total absence of subthreshold modes ($\xi = 0$ in (8)) and in injection current $J > 3J_{th}$, the laser generates single-mode of sub-Poissonian radiation ($F < 1$). The presence of subthreshold modes can substantially degrade the noise properties of the generated light. For a semiconductor laser with typical parameters in the free-lasing regime (with no external cavity, see Figure 17-A): $J = 3.5*J_{th}$; $J_{th} = 30$ мA; $\Delta\nu_{Int} = 150$ GHz we take from (8), (9) $r = 2.5$; $\chi = 0.72$; $\xi \cong 5.5.10^5$ (see [46,47]); $F >> 1$ [46, 47]. These estimates are confirm, so that the free-lasing regime of typical semiconductor lasers is substantially nonsingle-mode [67, 69, 73, 74].

However, if the noise contribution of the subthreshold modes is suppressed enough ($\xi < 1$), the condition $F < 1$ is not violated. This type of generation of a semiconductor laser with an external cavity at room temperature was realize and investigated in [46]. It was also proposed to regard a laser of such type a single-mode laser from the viewpoint of quantum optics [46]. Further in this chapter, the single-mode lasing will be understood just in this sense.

Unconditionally, the use of the diffraction grating gives the required suppression of the inherent subthreshold (long-distance) modes. But at the same time occurs a new problem: the external (long) cavity has its own mode structure as it is shown on Figure 17-B. These modes (short-distance modes), are spaced at $\Delta v_{Ext} = c/2L_{Ext} = 1.5$ GHz from the lasing mode, i.e., significantly closer than the intrinsic long-distance modes. Here $L_{Ext}=100$ mm is the length of the external cavity (the distance between the back cleavage plane and the grating). Because of small value of Δv_{Ext} the short-distance modes are not suppressed by the external cavity. This can greatly limit and in some cases eliminate the possibility of using a laser of such type in high precision experiments.

The formation of the modal structure of a semiconductor laser with an external cavity is analyzed by means of amplitude-phase equations [78]. The degree of coupling of the external and intrinsic cavities of the laser is described by the parameter T, which can be expressed through the relative increment of the threshold injection current $\delta J_{th}/J_{th}$ due to the installation of the grating:

$$T = (\ln \rho)\delta J_{th}/J_{th}, \tag{10}$$

where ρ describes the amplitude reflectance from the front cleavage.

Two main cases are distinguished, determined by the value of parameter T:

$$T < 4.6\, T_{min} ; \tag{11}$$

$$T > 1, \tag{12}$$

where $T_{min} = L_{Int}/L_{Ext}.$ $(T_{min} \ll 1)$.

In the case of weak-coupling, when inequality (11) holds, the external cavity does not form an additional system of modes, and thus the modal structure of the combined cavity is determined only by the intrinsic modes of the semiconductor laser. The modal composition in the weak-coupling regime is shown in Figure 17-C. In the opposite case of strong-coupling, when parameter T satisfies inequality (12), on the contrary, the external cavity determines the modal structure of the entire system, and the intrinsic modes of the semiconductor laser do not show up. In the intermediate case, of middle-coupling, both cavities participate in forming the complete system of modes.

On Figure 18 is shown our experimental setup for the investigations of noise of semiconductor injection laser with an external optical feedback. The laser radiation (780 nm) is detected by means of balance scheme that consist of the beamsplitter BS and photodiodes PD 1, PD 2. The external feedback is organized by a diffraction grating G. The analogous laser was used earlier for the investigation of the noise of strong selective reflected light (see Fig.13). Due to the dispersion of the grating, the reflected subthreshold modes in the ideal case do not return into own laser resonator. This gives the greater losses for the subthreshold modes compare with the generating mode [44,46,47].

For experimental values of L_{Int}=1mm; L_{Ext}=100 mm; $T_{min} = L_{Int}/L_{Ext} = 0.01$; ρ^2=10%; $\delta J_{th}/J_{th}$= -3%, we get from (10) that T = 0.035 < 4.6 T_{min} = 0.046, i.e., the laser operates in the weak-coupling regime (see (11)). The short-distance subthreshold modes don't exist in this case, because there are no corresponding external cavity modes. The diffraction grating in the external cavity also provides the suppression of the long-distance modes needed for the single-mode lasing [46, 78].

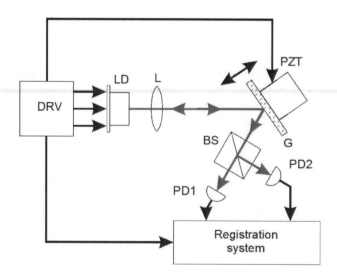

Figure 18. Setup for observation of squeezing.

For the injection current of about $4I_{th}$ the squeezing signal $S=(1-F)_{Exp} = -0.55$ dB of the Poissonian level (SNL) has been registered in the photocurrent fluctuations. From the (8), (9) it follows that the maximum possible reduction of the photodetection noise power at $I=4I_{th}$ is $(1-F)_{max}= -2.6$ dB. In our experiments, it was limited to the low quantum efficiency some of the used optical elements: diffraction grating, beamsplitter and photodiodes. The correction for the most essential losses in these elements gives the value of the observed squeezing of about -1.6 dB.

For experimental studies of suppression of the disturbing modes the lasing mode was passed through the scanning Fabry-Perot interferometer, which was tuning so as to pass only this mode. No appreciable changes of the squeezing were observed, that experimentally confirms the single-mode character of the realized lasing in terms of quantum optics. More detailed studies have also shown that the frequency fluctuations of the generating mode are one of the main factors limiting the observed squeezing.

Thus, the lasing described here has reduced (squeezed) fluctuations in the number of photons compared to the classical (coherent) light. The found regime of generation is completely singlemode from the point of view of quantum-optics as all disturbing modes in the spectrum of generation were suppressed, including the short-distance modes and the long-distance modes. This regime can also be called a totally singlemode quantum lasing (TSQL).

7. SQUEEZING OF QUANTUM FLUCTUATIONS FOR SELECTIVE REFLECTED LIGHT

As is well-known, the squeezing of quantum fluctuations of light takes place at its nonlinear interaction in the process of propagation through condensed media or ensembles of atoms [64, 79-82]. In section 4 is shown that the increase of a surface power density on the resonance interface leads to reduction of its reflectivity (see Figure 8). It was experimentally demonstrated that this reduction is accompanied by decrease of intensity fluctuations of the reflected light [55]. This registered "classical squeezing" and the relatively high selective reflection coefficient offer good possibilities for the squeezing of quantum fluctuations in reflected light. Here we will consider the experimental realization of these opportunities.

The next stage of the investigation is curried out on the experimental setup shown in Figure 13. Instead of the photodiode is used a balanced scheme photodetection (see Figure 18) that made it possible to compare with the high sensitivity the level of the photocurrents fluctuations with SNL [64, 82]. The used semiconductor laser operated in the region between weak and middle coupling regimes by $I \approx 3\ I_{th}$ (see subsection 6.2). Careful adjustment of the injection current, the degrees of coupling resonators and the position of a diffraction grating on minimum fluctuations of the reflected light was carried out before the onset of measurements. When this was reached a suppression of the influence of frequency fluctuations and subthreshold modes of the laser was sufficient for observation of the squeezing.

Figure 19 shows the typical time dependence of the squeezing signal $S=(1–F)_{Exp}$, for reflected light. The time intervals (0-100) seconds and (400-600) seconds correspond to non-resonant laser adjustment [46, 47]. It is good seen that in this case the signal S coincides with SNL i.e. the fluctuations of coherent radiation were recorded by the registration system on these intervals [83, 84].

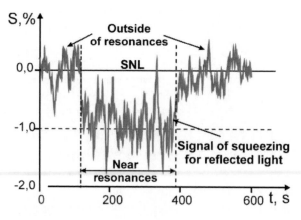

Figure 19. Squeezing of quantum fluctuations for selective reflected light.

At the interval (100-400) seconds the laser was tuned on a minimum of intensity fluctuations within the peaks of strong selective reflection [56]. As can be seen, the relative level of the photocurrent fluctuations is less in 1% than the SNL corresponding to detection of coherent light [84]. This reduction of fluctuations is determined by nonlinear properties of selective reflection resonances. As a result, the reflected photons flux becomes more regular. According to our estimates, which take into account a low quantum efficiency of the reflecting channel of the used optical system, the squeezing (reduction) of quantum (photons) fluctuations for the reflected radiation is about of 5% (-0.22 dB) in compare with the coherent light [61].

CONCLUSION

In this chapter the characteristics of a strong selective reflection of laser radiation from the interface glass – rubidium vapour in an inclined geometry are studied. More than 60% of the incident light (in terms of intensity) is reflected at the tops of the strong maxima. The comparable reflectivity in the orthogonal geometry needs the atomic concentrations a few orders higher. Under investigated conditions well-known sub-Doppler SR-resonances characteristic for the orthogonal incidence are not registered. Resonances of SR, observed here, are fairly broad (of about 1 GHz). They can be used, for example, in problems on variable spectral filters [85].

By increasing surface power density on the resonance interface a SR begins to saturate. This reduces the reflection coefficient and the fluctuations of the reflected light. In the reflection spectra also new nonlinear structure and asymmetry of saturation of selective TIR were recorded. Apart from the fundamental interest, these results may be used to enhance the non-linear properties of the resonance interfaces. This can be useful, for example, for the effective transformation of the classical and quantum fluctuations of the selective reflected light.

In the chapter it is shown that the use of the semiconductor laser with external cavity as a light source leads to the formation in selective reflection spectra the quasilevels of intensity. These quasilevels appear due to hopping of a generation frequency on modes of an external cavity. The study of quasilevels gives new information about transformation and controlling of informative and noise signals by their propagation through nontrivial and nonlinear optical systems.

It is also shown that at the optimum matching of external and own resonators realized a totally singlemode quantum lasing. This generation regime of a semiconductor laser at room temperature is characterized by reduced quantum (photon) fluctuations and complete suppression of the entire system of subthreshold modes, including modes of the external cavity. In this case, the development of theoretical and experimental approaches to the study of the fluctuations in complex cavities is also important. It can be assumed, that these approaches and the results can be extended to the investigation of the generation and evolution of fluctuations, including quantum, in complex oscillating (resonator) systems of different nature, having the properties of the additional suppression of interfering degrees of freedom (modes).

This chapter shows that nonlinear resonance interface can operate as an original intensity fluctuations microcontroller (damper) of a reflected light. Furthermore it is shown that this microcontroller can also decrease the quantum fluctuations of selective reflected light. Note that systems of such type were previously studied theoretically. A possibility of a significant (more than one order compared with a coherent light) suppression quantum fluctuations of amplitude for light transmitted through nonresonance nonlinear interface has been predicted [86].

Although the experimentally obtained in this chapter decrease in the amplitude of fluctuations is fairly small (-0.22dB) as compared to the values, achieved at the present time for the rubidium when operating in transmission (-2dB [87]; -3dB [88]; >2dB [89]), but of high importance is the fundamental aspect of the problem – squeezing in reflected light. The nonlinear reflective systems have a set of paradoxical properties: the classical and quantum theories of its description give directly opposite behaviors of the phase fluctuations [90]. Beside this the amplitude and phase of quantum fluctuations of the incident light can be separated and directed into reflection and transmission channels [91]. It should be recalled that the laser systems with optoelectronic feedback also have some paradoxical properties in terms of comparison of classical and quantum optics [92-95].

Thus, the investigations in this chapter complement and contribute to the development of optoelectronics, classical and quantum optics.

REFERENCES

[1]   R. W. Wood, R. V. The selective reflection of monochromatic light by mercury vapor. *Philos. Mag.* 1909, V.18, 187.

[2]   Lauriston, A. C.; Welsh, H.L. Selective reflection from the vapors of the alkali metals. *Canad. J. Phys.* 1951, V.39, 217-226.

[3]   Cojan, J. L. Contribution a l'etude de la reflection selective sur les vapeurs de mercure de la radiation de resonance du mercure, *Ann. Phys.* (Paris). 1954, V. 9, 385-440.

[4]   Chen,C. L.; Phelps, A. V. Self-broadening of cesium resonance lines at 8521 and 8944 Å. *Phys. Rev.* 1968, V. 173, No.1, 62-69.

[5]   Senitzky, B. Optical filter using a vapor mirror. *Appl. Phys. Lett.* 1974, V. 24, No. 2, 68-70.

[6]   Guo, J.; Gallagher, A.; Cooper, J. Lorentz-Lorenz shift in an inhomogeneously broadened medium. *Opt. Commun.* 1996, V.131, No. 4-6, 219-222.

[7]   Wang, P.; Gallagher, A.; Cooper, J. *Selective reflection by Rb. Phys. Rev.* 1997, V.A 56, 1598–1606.

[8]   Woerdman, J. P.; Schuurmans, M. F. H. Spectral narrowing of selective reflection from sodium vapour. *Opt. Commun.* 1975, V. 14, 248-251.

[9]   Schurmans, M. F. H. Spectral narrowing of selective reflection. *J. Physique.* 1976, Vol. 37, 469-485.

[10] Burgmans, A. L. J.; Woerdman J. P. Selective reflection from sodium vapour at low densities. J. *Physique.* 1976, Vol.37, 677-681.

[11] Sautenkov, V. A.; Velichasnskii, V. L.; Zibrov, A. S.; Luk'yanov, V. I.; Nikitin, V. V. Tyurikov, D. A. Intra-Doppler resonances of the cesium D_2 line in a selective specular reflection profile. *Sov. J. Quantum Electron.* 1981, Vol.11, No.9, 1131-1134.

[12] Akul'shin, A. M.; Velichanskii, V. L.; Zibrov, A. S.; Nikitin, V. I.; Sautenkov, V. A.; Yurkin, E. K.; Senkov, N. V. Collisional broadening of intra-Doppler resonances of selective reflection on the D_2 line of cesium. *Sov. Phys.-JETP Letters.* 1982, Vol.36, No.7, 303-307.

[13] Vartanyan, T. A. Resonant reflection of intense optical radiation from a low-density gaseous medium, *Sov. Phys.-JETP,* Vol.61, No.4, 674-677, 1985.

[14] Xiao Lian-tuan, Zhao Jian-ming, Li Chang-yong, Jia Suo-tang, and Zhou Guo-sheng. Precise measurement of density-dependent shift by wavelength modulation reflection Spectroscopy. *Chinese Physics.* 2001, Vol.10, No.8, 716-719.

[15] Sautenkov, V. A.; Varzhapetyan, T. S.; Li, H.; Sarkisyan, D.; Scully, M. O. Selective reflection of a laser beam from a dilute rubidium vapor. *Journal of Russian Laser Research (Moscow).* 2010, Vol.31, No.3, 270-275.

[16] Failache, H.; Saltiel, S.; Fichet, M.; Bloch, D.; Ducloy M. Resonant coupling in the van der Waals interaction between an excited alkali atom and a dielectric surface: an experimental study via stepwise selective reflection spectroscopy. *Eur. Phys. J.* 2003, Vol.D23, 237-255.

[17] Bloch, D; Ducloy, M. Atom-wall interaction. *Advances in At., Mol., and Optical Phys.* 2005, Vol.50, No.1.

[18] Laliotis, A.; Silans, T. P.; Maurin, I.; Ducloy, M.; Bloch, D. *Casimir-Polder forces in the presence of thermally excited surface modes.* arXiv:1403.3898v1 physics.atom-ph.

[19] Letokhov, V. S. Selective feedback for broadband lasers. *Kr. Soobshch. Fiz. FIAN* (Moscow). 1970, Vol.11, 14-17.

[20] Bolger, B.; Weysenfeld, C. Locking of organic dye laser frequency to atomic resonance lines. *IEEE J. of Quantum Electron.* 1972, Vol.8, No.6, 529 529.

[21] Velichansky, V. L.; Zibrov, A. S.; Nikitin, V. V.; Sautenkov, V. A.; Malyshev, V. K.; Kharisov, G. G. Semiconductor laser with [133]Cs vapor external selective mirror. *Sov. J. Quantum Electron.* 1978, Vol.8, No.7, 836-840.

[22] Ito, T.; Hashi, T.; Yabuzaki, T. Frequency stabilization of an AlGaAs laser using selective reflection spectrum. *Opt. Commun.* 1991, Vol.82, No.5-6, 473-476.

[23] Rabi, O. A.; Amy-Klein, A.; Saltiel, S.; Ducloy, M. Three-Level Non-linear Selective Reflection at a Dielectric/Cs Vapour Interface. *Europhys. Lett.* 1994, Vol.25, No.8, 579.

[24] Van Kampen, H.; Sautenkov, V. A.; Eliel, E. R.; Woerdman, J. P. Probing the spatial dispersion in a dense atomic vapor near a dielectric interface. *Phys. Rev.* 1998, Vol.A58, No.6, 4473-4478.

[25] Yan-Ting Zhao; Jie Ma; Li-Rong Wang; Jian-Ming Zhao; Lian-Tuan Xiao; Suo-Tang Jia. Spectral hole-burning in pump–probe studies of nonlinear selective reflection spectroscopy. *J. Phys. B: At. Mol. Opt. Phys.* 2005, Vol.38, 3037-3042. doi: 10.1088/0953-4075/38/16/014

[26] Zhao Yan-Ting; Zhao Jian-Ming; Huang Tao; Xiao Lian-Tuan and Jia Suo-Tang. Experimental Observation of Autler–Townes Splitting in Sub-Doppler Selective Reflection Spectroscopy. *Chinese Phys. Lett.* 2005, Vol.22, 1668.

[27] Sautenkov, V. A.; Rostovtsev, Y. V.; Eliel E. R. Observation of narrow Autler-Townes components in the resonant response of a dense atomic gas. *Phys. Rev.* 2008, Vol.A 78, No.1, 013802.

[28] Li, H.; Sautenkov, V. A.; Rostovtsev, Y. V.; Scully, M. O. Excitation dependence of resonance line self-broadening at different atomic densities. *J. Phys. B: At. Mol. Opt. Phys.* 2009, Vol.42, 065203. doi: 10.1088/0953-4075/42/6/065203

[29] Nienhuis, G.; Schuller, F.; Ducloy, M. Nonlinear selective reflection from an atomic vapor at arbitrary incidence angle. *Phys. Rev.* 1988, Vol.A 38, 5197-5205.

[30] Akul'shin, A. M.; Velichanskii, V. L.; Zherdev, A. I.; Zibrov, A. S.; Malakhova, V. U.; Nikitin, V. A.; Sautenkov, V. A.; Kharisov, G. G.

Selective reflection from the glass-gas interface at high angles. *Sov. J. Quantum Electron.* 1989, Vol.19, No.3, 416-419.

[31] Boissel, P.; Kerherve, F. Absorption de lumiere par des atomes dans une onde evanescente. *Opt. Commun.* 1981, Vol.37, No.6, 397-402.

[32] Simoneau, P.; Le, B. S.; De Arauio, C. B.; Bloch, D.; Lios Leite, I. R.; Ducloy M. Doppler-free evanescent wave spectroscopy. *Opt. Commun.* 1986, Vol.59, No.2, 103-106.

[33] Bordo, V. G.; Rubahn H.-G. Two-photon evanescent-wave spectroscopy of alkali-metal atoms. *Phys. Rev.* 1999, Vol.A 60, 1538–1548.

[34] Kondo, R.; Tojo, S.; Fujimoto, T.; Hasuo, M. Shift and broadening in attenuated total reflection spectra of the hyperfine-structure-resolved D2 line of dense rubidium vapor. *Phys. Rev.* 2006, Vol.A73, 062504

[35] Bykovskii, Yu. A.; Velichanskii, V. L.; Egorov, V. K.; Zibrov, A. S.; Maslov, V. A. Optical pumping and nonlinear effects in the spectroscopy of the cesium D_2 line. *JETP Letters.* 1974, Vol.19, No.11, 345-346.

[36] Akul'shin, A. M.; Vartanyan, T. A.; Velichanskii, V. L.; Gamidov, R. G.; Sautenkov, V. A. Nonlinear effects in selective reflection from resonant gas. *Izv. Akad. Nauk SSSR, Ser. Fiz.* (Moscow). 1989, Vol.53, No.6, 1122-1124.

[37] Guo, J.; Cooper, J.; Gallagher, A.; Lewenstein, M. Theory of selective reflection spectroscopy. *Opt. Commun.* 1994, Vol.110, 197-208.

[38] Walser, R.; Cooper, J.; Zoller P. Saturated absorption spectroscopy using diode-laser phase noise, *Phys. Rev.* 1994, Vol.A 50, 4303–4309.

[39] Sarkisyan, D.; Bloch, D.; Papoyan, A; Ducloy M. Sub-Doppler spectroscopy of sub-micron thin Cs vapour layer. *Opt. Comm.* 2001, Vol.200, 201-208.

[40] Dutier, G.; Yarovittskii, A.; Saltiel, S.; Papoyan, A.; Sarkisyan, D.; Bloch, D.; Ducloy M. Collapse and revival of a Dicke-type coherent narrowing in a sub-micron thick vapor cell transmission spectroscopy. *Europhys. Lett.* 2003, Vol.63, No.1, 35-41.

[41] Hamdi, I.; Todorov P.; Yarovitski, A. Dutier, G.; Maurin, I.; Saltie, S.; Li, Y.; Lezama, A. Varzhapetyan, T.; Sarkisyan, D.; Gorza, M.-P.; Fichet, M.; Bloch, D.; Ducloy, M. Laser Spectroscopy with Nanometric Gas Cells: Distance Dependence of Atom–Surface Interaction and Collisions under Confinement. *Laser Physics.* 2005, Vol.15, No.7, 987-996.

[42] McIntyre, D. H.; Fairchild, C. E.; Cooper, J.; Walser, R. Diode-laser noise spectroscopy of rubidium. *Optics Letters.* 1993, Vol.18, No.21, 1816-1818.

[43] Peterman, K. *Laser Diodes Modulation and Noise.* Kluwer Academic Publshers. 1991.

[44] Wieman, C. E.; Hollberg, L. Using diode lasers for atomic physics. *Rev. Sci. Instr.* 1991, Vol.62., 1-20.

[45] Trifonov, A. S.; Usachev, P. A. Quantum correlations of the pump and radiation noise of a semiconductor laser near its threshold. *JETP.* 1995, Vol. 81, No. 4, 687.

[46] Trifonov, A. S. When May a Diode Laser be Regarded as a Single-Mode Laser from the Viewpoint of Quantum Optics? *Optics and Spectroscopy.* 1999, Vol. 86, No.1, 121-125. http://www. rusnanonet.ru/nns/23881

[47] Fofanov, Ya. A.; Sokolov, I. V. Sub-Poissonian single-mode lasing in a semiconductor laser with an external cavity. *Journal of Optical Technology.* 2003, Vol.70, No.1, 38-41. http://www.opticsinfobase. org/jot/home.cfm

[48] Fofanov, Ya. A. Selective reflection of obliquely incident polarized light. *Sov. J. Quantum Electron.* 2009, Vol.39, No.6, 585-590. DOI 10.1070/QE1991v021n08ABEH003975   http://www.turpion.org/php/paper

[49] Fofanov Ya. A. Optical Saturation of Strong Selective Reflection. *Universal Journal of Physics and Application.* 2013, 1(4): 370-375. DOI: 10.13189/ujpa.2013.010402. http://www.hrpub.org.

[50] Daniel A. Steck, *"Rubidium 85 D Line Data,"* available online at http://steck.us/alkalidata (revision 2.1.6, 20 September 2013).

[51] Daniel A. Steck, *"Rubidium 87 D Line Data,"* available online at http://steck.us/alkalidata (revision 2.1.4, 23 December 2010).

[52] Vartanyan, T.A. *Optics and Spectroscopy.* 1990, 68, 625.

[53] Schuller, F.; Gorceix, O.; Ducloy, M. *Phys. Rev. A.* 1993, 47, 519.

[54] Vartanyan, T.A.; Weis, A. *Phys. Rev. A.* 2001, V. 63, 1.

[55] Fofanov, Ya. A. Transformation of intensity fluctuations in nonlinear reflection of light. *Optics and Spectroscopy.* 2003, Vol.94, No.5, 802-804. link.springer.com/article/10.1134%2F1.1576854

[56] Fofanov, Ya. A. Controlling the Intensity and Fluctuations of Light upon Its Selective Reflection, *Optics and Spectroscopy.* 2005, Vol.99, No.3, 457-458. link.springer.com/article/10.1134%2F1.1576854

[57] Gibbs, H. M. Optical Bistability. *Controlling Light With Light.* Academic Press, Orlando. 1985.

[58] Vartanyan, T. A. Optical Control of Longitudinal Periodic Structures Near the Boundary of a Rarefied Resonance Medium. *Optics and Spectroscopy.* 2000, Vol.88, No.4, 564-567. link.springer.com/ article/10.1134%2F1.1576854

[59] Sautenkov, V. A. Line shapes of atomic transitions in excited dense gas. *Laser Phys. Lett.* 2011, Vol.8, No.11, 771–781. DOI 10.1002/ lapl.201110070 771.

[60] Fofanov, Ya. A., "On nonlinear effects under the conditions of selective total internal reflection," *J. RAS Nauchnoe priborostroenie* 18(1), 35-39 (2008). http://www.rusnanonet.ru/nns/23881

[61] Fofanov, Ya. A. New nonlinear phenomena under conditions of strong selective reflection. In ICONO 2010: International Conference on Coherent and Nonlinear Optics. Edited by Claude Fabre, Victor Zadkov, Konstantin Drabovich. *Proceedings of SPIE.* Vol. 7993. (SPIE, Bellingham, WA 2011) 79930O (2011); doi:10.1117/12.882693.

[62] Sokolov, I. V.; Fofanov, Ya. A. On the Admissible Natural Linwidth of Laser Radiation Necessry for the Observation of Squeezing in the Case of Self-Phase Modulation in a Resonant Medium. *Optics and Spectroscopy.* 1996, Vol.81, No.4, 635-637. link.springer.com/ article/10.1134%2F1.1576854

[63] Alferov, Zh. *Physics and Life.* Nauka, Moscow, 2000.

[64] Bachor, H.-A., Ralph, T. C. A. *Guide to Experiments in Quantum Optics.* Wiley-VCH, Weinheim. 2004.

[65] Yamamoto, Y. Generation of squeezed light from semiconductor laser and its precision measurements. *Phys. Scr.* 1998, V. 76, P. 103.

[66] Richardson, W. H.; Yamamoto, Y. Quantum correlation between junction-voltage fluctuation and the photon number fluctuation in a semiconductor laser. *Phys. Rev. Lett.* 1991, V. 66, P. 1963.

[67] Marin, F.; Bramati, A.; Giacobino, E.; Zhang, T.-C.; Poizat, J.-Ph. Roch, J.-F.; ; Grangier, P. Squeezing and intermode correlation in laser diodes. *Phys. Rev. Lett.* 1995, V. 75, P. 4606.

[68] Kitching J.; Yariv A.; Shevy Y. Room Temperature Generation of Amplitude Squeezed Light from a Semiconductor Laser with Weak Optical Feedback. *Phys. Rev. Lett.*1995, V. 74, P. 3372-3375.

[69] Kitching J.; Provenzano D.; Yariv A. Generation of amplitude-squeezed light from a room-temperature Fabry-Perot semiconductor laser. *Opt. Lett.* 1995. V. 20. P. 2526-2528.

[70] Richrdson   W.H.;   Shelby   R.M.;   Nonclassical   Light   From   a
      Semiconductor-Laser Operating at 4-K. *Phys. Rev. Lett.* 1990, V. 64, P.
      400-403.

[71] Kim J.S.; Kan H.F.; Yamamoto Y. Macroscopic Coulomb-Blocade
      Effect in a Constant-Current-Driven Light-Emitting Diode. *Phys. Rev. B.*
      1995, V. 52, 2008-2012.

[72] Freeman, M.J.; Wang, H.; Steel, D.G.; Craig, R.; Scifres, D. R.
      Wavelength-tunable amplitude-squeezed light from a room-temperature
      quantum-well laser. *Optics Letters.* 1995, V. 18, 2141-2143.

[73] Zhang, T.; Poizat, J.-Ph.; Grelu, P.; Roch, J.-F.; Grangier, P.; Marin, F.;
      Bramati, A.; Jost, V.; Levenson, M.D.; Giacobino, E. Quantum noise of
      free running and externally-stabilized laser diodes. *Quant. Semiclass.
      Opt.* 1995, V. 7, P.601-613.

[74] Poizat, J.P.; Grangier, P. Observation of anticorrelated modal noise in a
      quasi-single-mode laser diode with Michelson interferometer. *JOSA B.*
      1997, V. 14 (11),. P. 2772-2781.

[75] Agrawal, G. P. Mode-partition-noise and intensity correlation in a two-
      mode semiconductor laser. *Physical Review A.* 1988, V. 37, P. 2488-
      2494.

[76] Inoue, S.; Lathi, S.; Yamamoto, Y. Longitudinal-mode-partition noise
      and amplitude squeezing in semiconductor lasers. *JOSA B.* 1997, V. 14,
      P. 2761-2766.

[77] Richardson, W.H.; Yamamoto, Y. Quantum measurement of the Photon
      Number via the Junction Voltage in a Semiconductor-Laser. *Phys. Rev.
      A.* 1991, V. 44, P. 7702-7716.

[78] Fofanov, Ya. A.; Sokolov, I. V. Single-mode amplitude squeezing in a
      semiconductor laser at 780 nm. *Optics and Spectroscopy.* 2001, V. 91
      (4), P. 519 - 525. http://link.springer.com/article/10.1134/1.1412665

[79] Slusher, R.E.; Hollberg, L.V.; Yurke, B.; Mertz, J.C.; Valley, J.F.
      Observation of Squeezed States Generated by Four-Wave Mixing in an
      Optical Cavity. *Phys. Rev. Lett.* 1985, 55, 2409-2412.

[80] Teich, M. C.; Saleh, B. E. A. Squeezed state of light. Quantum Optics:
      Journ. EOS Part B 1989, 1(2), 153-191.

[81] Davidovich, L.; Sub-Poissonian processes in quantum optics. *Rev. Mod.
      Phys.* 1996, 68(1), 127–173.

[82] Scully, M. O., Zubairy, M. S. *Quantum optics.* University press.
      Cambridge. 2001, ch. 4.

[83] Glauber, R. J.; Optical Coherence and Photon Statistics. In *Quantum Optics and Electronics*. Ed. DeWitt, C.; Blandin, A.; Cohen-Tannou, C. New York. Gordon and Breach. 1965, 63.

[84] Fofanov, Ya. A. Reduction of fluctuations of selective reflected light. *J. RAS Nauchnoe priborostroenie*. 2009, 19(1), 27–29. http://www.rusnanonet.ru/nns/23881

[85] Sautenkov, V. A.; Li, H.; Gubin, M. A.; Rostovtsev, Yu. V.; Scully, M. O. Variable spectral filter based on optically saturated selective reflection. *Laser Physics*. 2011, Vol. 21, No. 1, 153–157. DOI: 10.1134/S1054660X1101018X

[86] Belinsky, A V. Transformation of quantum fluctuations of the intensity in nonlinear systems with saturation, *Sov. J. Quantum Electron*. 1991, V. 21 (1), 75–79. DOI 10.1070/QE1991v021n01ABEH003716

[87] Agha, I. H.; Messin, G.; Grangier P. Generation of pulsed and continuous-wave squeezed light with ^{87}Rb vapor. *Optics Express*. 2010, 18 (5), 4198-4205. http://dx.doi.org/10.1364/OE.18.004198

[88] Valente, S. B. P.; Failache, H.; Lezama, A. Polarization squeezing of light by single passage through an atomic vapor. *Phys. Rev.* A 84, 2011, 033851. http://dx.doi.org/10.1103/PhysRevA.84.033851

[89] Horrom, T.; Novikova, I.; Mikhailov E. *All-atomic source of squeezed vacuum with full pulse-shape control.* arXiv:1204.3967v1 [quant-ph] 18 Apr 2012.

[90] Belinsky, A. V.; Granovskiy, A. A. Paradox of a nonlinear beam splitter and selection of photon fluctuations. *JETP Letters,* 2011, 93 (9), 495-497. DOI 10.1134/S106377611312011X

[91] Belinsky, A. V; Volkov, D. V.; Dmitriev, A. V.; Shulman, M. Kh. Paradox of a nonlinear beam splitter and its resolution. *JETP*. 2013, 117 (5), 771-783. DOI 10.1134/S106377611312011X

[92] Shapiro, J H; Saplakoglu, G; Ho, S -T; Kumar, P; Saleh, B E A; Teich, M C. Theory of light detection in the presence of feedback. *JOSA* B. 1987, 4 (10), 1604-1620. http://dx.doi.org/10.1364/JOSAB.4.001604

[93] Fofanov, Ya. A. *Sov. J. Journal of Communications Technology and Electronics*. 1988, 336, 171. http://link.springer.com/journal/volumes AndIssues/11487

[94] Fofanov, Ya. A. Analysis of experimental observations of a sub-Poisson field. *Sov. J. Quantum Electron*. 1991, 21 (8), 873-876. DOI 10.1070/QE1991v021n08ABEH003975
http://www.turpion.org/php/paper.phtml?journal_id=qe&paper_id=3975

[95] Klyshko, D. N.; A Masalov, A. V. Photon noise: observation, squeezing, interpretation. *Physics-Uspekhi.* 1995, 38 (11), 1203–1230. DOI: 10.1070/PU1995v038n11ABEH000117

BIOGRAPHICAL SKETCH

Name:
Yakov A. Fofanov.

Affiliation:
Main scientific researcher, Institute for Analytical Instrumentation RAS, St.-Petersburg, Russia.

Date of Birth:
June 25, 1946

Education:
Physicist, St-Petersburg State University, Leningrad (now St-Petersburg), Russia, 1974.

Certifications:
Ph.D. (Physics), St-Petersburg State University, Leningrad (now St-Petersburg), Russia, 1981.
Doctor of Science (Physics), St-Petersburg State University, 1995.

Address (office):
Institute for Analytical Instrumentation RAS, Ivana Chernykh St., 31-33, St-Petersburg, 198095, Russia.
(Институт Аналитического приборостроения РАН, ул. Ивана Черных, 31-33, С.-Петербург, 198095, Россия).

Research and Professional Experience:
- Stabilizes lasers, noise of laser radiation, high sensitive optical measurements, quantum optics, magnetooptics, life science (a little). For the first time has realized threshold sensitivity (on the SNL) for polarization-optical measurements with strong polarization modulation of probing laser radiation and differential registration of

informative signals (Prog. SPIE, Vol. 1811, p. 413 (1992)) These methods for the first time have been applied to the studies of:

- Polarization characteristics of TIR prisms of high precision (JOSA, 1995);
- Fluorite crystals of high optical and structural homogenity (JOT (Russia), 1998).
- A fine rearrangement of the domain structure of magnetized iron borate crystals (JOT (Russia), 2013);
- Small polarization response of delute ferrofluids (ICONO, 2013).
- One of the first has watched the sub-Poissonian generation of a helium-neon laser in optoelectronic feedback loop photodetector-pumping. (1985).
- For the first time has suggested the analogy between biological evolution and the magnetization process (Natural Science, April, 2013).
- Scientific Adviser of two dissertations Doctor of Science (Physics), 2003, 2009.

Professional Appointments:
Institute for Analytical Instrumentation RAS.

Honors:
- Medal, "A 300-anniversary of Saint Petersburg ", 2003;
- Honorary title of "Veteran of Labor", 2006.
- Honorary signs and honorary diplomas of the Russian Government and the RAS Presidium.

Publications Last 3 Years:
1. Ya. A. Fofanov. "New nonlinear phenomena under conditions of strong selective reflection". In ICONO 2010: International Conference on Coherent and Nonlinear Optics. Edited by Claude Fabre, Victor Zadkov, Konstantin Drabovich. Proceedings of SPIE. Vol. 7993. (SPIE, Bellingham, WA 2011) 799300 (2011); doi:10.1117/ 12.882693. Date: 6 January 2011.
2. Ya. A. Fofanov, A. S. Kuraptsev, and I. M. Sokolov. Dispersion of the dielectric permittivity of dense and ultracold atomic gases. Phys. Rev. A. 84. 053811-1 - 053811-9 (2011).

3. Ya. A. Fofanov, I. V. Pleshakov, and Yu. I. Kuz'min. Laser polarization-optical detection of the magnetization process of a magnetically ordered crystal. Journal of Optical Technology, Vol. 80, Issue 1, pp. 64-67 (2013). http://dx.doi.org/10.1364/JOT.80.000064

4. Fofanov, Y. (2013) On the analogy in evolution processes and the behavior of a magnetically ordered systems. Natural Science, Vol.5, No.4A, 14-17 (2013). doi: 10.4236/ns.2013.54A003. http://www.scirp.org/journal/ns/

5. Ya. A. Fofanov, A. S. Kuraptsev, I. M. Sokolov, M. D. Havey. Spatial distribution of optically induced atomic excitation in a dense and cold atomic ensemble. Phys. Rev. A. 87, 063839 (2013).

6. Ya. A. Fofanov. Optical Saturation of Strong Selective Reflection. Universal Journal of Physics and Application 1(4): 370-375, 2013. DOI: 10.13189/ujpa.2013.010402. http://www.hrpub.org.

7. Ya.A. Fofanov, E.E. Bibik, I.V. Pleshakov, P.M. Agruzov. Precision Laser Detection of Magnetization Processes of Magnetically Ordered Substances. Int'l Conference on Coherent and Nonlinear Optics (ICONO/LAT 2013) Moscow, Russia, June, 18-22, 2013. Technical digest, ICONO-08 Ultrafast Phenomena and High-Precision Measurementsp, p. 12-13 (2013).

INDEX

S

On Figure 2 we can see the qualitative picture selective reflection of coherent light in inclined geometry. Light is polarized in the incidence plane (parallel polarization). The angle of incidence is determined only by the angular position of a reflecting cell. At the presence of a resonance gas, the critical angle of TIR and Brewster angle depend on the detuning of the optical frequency relative to the center of line. This leads to significant changes in the intensity of reflected light when adjusting the frequency. In particular a resonant approaching of the critical angle of TIR to the angle of incidence is accompanied by a sharp increase in the reflection coefficient.

3. LINEAR SR IN INCLINED GEOMETRY

3.1. Comparable Study of SR for Different Angles of Incidence and Polarizations

Figure 3 shows three typical dependences of the reflection coefficient R on the laser frequency (reflection spectra), which correspond to three different angles of incidence and the parallel polarization [48]. Figure 4 shows the relative intensity of light transmitted through the absorption cell (absorption spectrum). The hyperfine components of D2-lines of ^{85}Rb and ^{87}Rb isotopes (see inset on Figure 4) correspond to peaks a`, A`, B`, and b` in absorption spectra, which are used to calibrate frequency axes.

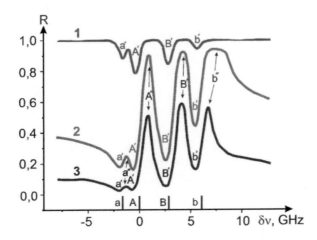

Figure 3. Experimental spectra of strong SR for parallel polarization.

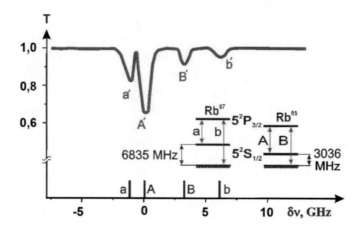

Figure 4. Absorption spectrum for Rubidium at 780 nm.

The shapes of reflection curves 1-3 in Figure 3 noticeably differ from each other. Reflection spectrum 1 corresponds to the angle of incidence 64° at which TIR conditions are fulfilled outside resonance lines or in the absence of Rb vapour because the nonresonance critical TIR angle is 34.6^O. One can see that curve 1 virtually coincides with the absorption curve: dips a`, A`, B`, and b` on the reflection spectrum 1 are similar to dips a`, A`, B`, and b` in absorption spectrum on Figure 4. This gives us the grounds for the suggestion that the dips in curves 1 are formed by the violation of TIR due to absorption in the resonance gas. More exactly radiation is scattered by atoms interacting with the evanescent wave existing under TIR conditions [29-34].

Reflection spectrum 2 in Figure 3 corresponds to the angle of incidence 34° at which TIR condition is not fulfilled outside resonance line (nonresonance R = 0.40). Curve 2 strongly differs from curve 1: the reflection coefficient at the bottom of dips a``, A``, B``, and b`` are considerably decreased, but at the same time the reflection peaks a``, A``, B``, and b`` are appeared. The formation of reflection peaks is especially well observed by comparing peaks A``, B`` with peak b``. The top of peak b`` is still flat because at his frequency the conditions close to frustrated TIR is fulfilled. The reflection coefficient at the tops of peaks A`` and B`` are somewhat smaller, and these tops are sharper as compare with b``. Peaks a`` for all curves are weaker, that can be explained by the influence of neighbour peak A``.

Spectrum 3 in Figure 3 demonstrates pronounced resonance reflection in the inclined geometry. This spectrum corresponds to the angle of incidence 33° at which the reflection coefficient outside resonance lines is 0.10.

A comparison of spectra 2 and 3 shows that the intensities of peaks A`` and B``
decrease with decreasing the angle of incidence, which is mainly explained by
the deviation from conditions close to TIR. Nevertheless, the resonance
reflection coefficient at the top of peak B`` of spectrum 3 exceeds 60 %, while
the contrast of this resonance (the ratio of the peak intensity to the pedestal
intensity) is no less than 5.

The resonance change in the refraction index of an atomic ensemble leads
to the corresponding modification of the Brewster angle and the reflection
conditions approach to the Brewster reflection (BR), more exactly to pseudo
BR because resonance gas has absorption (scattering). Due to the reduction of
the angle of incidence the reflection conditions at dips a`, A`, B` and b` in
spectrum 3 in Figure 3 are much closer to pseudo BR than in spectrum 2. As a
result, the value of R drastically changes on passing from the dips between the
peaks to tops of them. This change for peaks A`` and B`` in spectrum 3 exceeds
20 and 10, respectively.

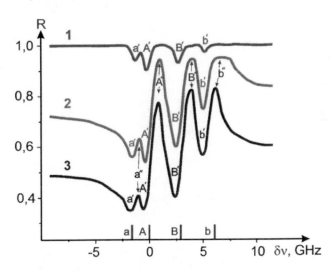

Figure 5. Experimental spectra of strong SR for orthogonal polarization.

Submitted in Figure 5 reflection spectra for orthogonal orientation have
the same characteristics as for the above considered parallel orientation. So the
spectrum 1 is similar to the absorption spectrum on Figure 4. In the spectra 2
and 3 are retained the main features - strong selective reflection on the tops of
the peaks A`` and B``. But there are some differences. We see that the
reflection coefficient at the bottom of dips a`, A`, B`, and b` in spectra 2, 3 for

the parallel orientation is several times smaller than the corresponding reflection coefficient for the orthogonal orientation. This can be explained by that reflection conditions at the bottom of dips in Figure 3 are approaching to pseudo BR whereas in the case of orthogonal polarization as is well known, BR does not exist.

3.2. Elementary Theoretical Model and Calculations

The theoretical consideration is based on the model of a two-level atom interacting with a plane light wave. It is assumed that the atom has only the ground state and one excited state, no transitions occurs to other levels, and the resonance transition is not saturated by a laser field. On these assumptions the correction to the wave vector k of a resonance light wave, which propagates through the ensemble of atoms, is found (compare with [34]):

$$\Delta k = \Delta k' + i\Delta k'',$$

(1)

$$\Delta k' = -\Delta\mu \, \Delta k'',$$

(2)

$$\Delta k'' = k_0'' n_0 f / [\Gamma_{21}(1+\Delta\mu^2)],$$

(3)

where n_0 is the concentration of atoms; f is the oscillator strength; Γ_{21} is the homogeneous half-width of the atomic line; $\Delta\mu = (v-v_a)/\Gamma_{21}$ is the dimensionless detuning of the field frequency v from the atomic frequency v_a, and k_0'' is a numerical coefficient determined by fundamental constants and the chosen system of units.

The real experimental situation, in which selective reflection was determined by four resonance lines, was described by calculating the total correction to the wave vector

$$\Delta k = \sum_{k=1}^{4} g_i \, \Delta k_i,$$

(4)